By AARON E. KLEIN

The Hidden Contributors:
Black Scientists and Inventors in America

Threads of Life:
Genetics from Aristotle to DNA

Test Tubes and Beakers:
Chemistry for Young Experimenters
(*With E. H. Coulson and A. E. J. Trinder*)

Transistors and Circuits:
Electronics for Young Experimenters
(*With W. E. Pearce*)

THE HIDDEN CONTRIBUTORS

The Hidden Contributors

Black Scientists and

Inventors in America

AARON E. KLEIN

1971

DOUBLEDAY & COMPANY, INC.
Garden City, New York

Library of Congress Catalog Card Number 76–157605
Copyright © 1971 by Aaron E. Klein
All Rights Reserved
Printed in the United States of America
First Edition

The author wishes to acknowledge the following individuals and organizations who generously gave of their time and knowledge and helped to make this book possible.

The staff of the Schomburg Collection in New York City, Mr. M. A. Harris, Mr. Alfred Webre, Jr., of the Bahamas Agricultural Institute, the staff of *Sugar y Azucar*, The First Church of Christ Congregationalist, Lynn, Massachusetts, the staff of the Edison National Historic Site in West Orange, New Jersey, and to Mr. Garrett A. Morgan, Jr., who supplied the author with many pictures and materials on his father.

CONTENTS

AN INTRODUCTION
AS DEDICATION

When I was a boy in Georgia, my parents had a small grocery store in an Atlanta ghetto called Peoplestown. We lived in a house two blocks from the store and one block from an invisible line that separated Peoplestown from the houses in which the white people lived.

I had a collection of chemical glassware and assorted bottles and cans which I claimed to be a chemistry laboratory. And when I was so inclined I blew up hydrogen generators; copper-plated my father's silver tie clasp; made gunpowder and invisible ink; effected magical color changes with acids, bases, and indicators; and concocted whatever else my erratic curiosity impelled me to do.

As the neighborhood boys heard about my chemistry laboratory, they asked to be shown its wonders, and this I gladly did for their "ooh's" and "ah's" and other expressions of awe did much for my budding ego.

Some of the boys in Peoplestown also heard of my chemistry laboratory, and they too wanted to know what went on there. So they, too, came to my home to see clear phenolphthalein solution turn red when clear ammonia water was added to it, and to see glowing steel wool burst into flame when put into a bottle of oxygen. And their "ooh's" and "ah's" and other expressions of awe were the same as those uttered by the white boys, and they had the same effect on my budding ego.

It did not at first occur to me that the presence of black boys from Peoplestown among the beakers, bottles, and assorted chemicals constituted a violation of the southern racial mystique. But that a violation had occurred was made very clear one evening as I walked the two blocks from my parents' store to the house. As I crossed the invisible line from Peoplestown to the nameless white area, I was surrounded by a group of white boys, many of whom had observed my chemical demonstrations.

Through the darkness I could see mouths drawn in tight lines of anger, the same mouths that had hung open in awe at my chemical displays. Few words were spoken. One boy simply wanted to know who had told me I could invite niggers to come out of Niggertown and enter their streets. From what omnipotent source came the permission to let black boys cross the line was not made clear. But what was made most clear, even though it was not said, was that I had dared to invite black boys to share the same wonders that the white boys had seen in my little chemistry laboratory.

They parted to let me pass, and as soon as my back was to them, the hitting started. The blows came down on my head, neck, and back. Somehow I ended up face down on the ground, and their kicks and spits were punctuated with cries of "nigger lover!"

It was over in a matter of minutes, and as they hit, kicked, and ran, I thought of the Peoplestown boys and of an unschooled old, black carpenter I had known who had, although neither he nor I knew it at the time, demonstrated the Pythagorean theorem and other theorems of geometry with a carpenter's square and a pencil.

The black carpenter had never been able to enter into a world in which he could have learned of Euclid, Phythagoras, and whatever else his abilities and desire to know might have impelled him to investigate. But many of his brothers have crossed the line in all its guises, from an invisible line between neighborhoods to the white line a governor of a state caused to be painted in front of the door of a university.

So, in the matter of dedication, this book is for those such as the old carpenter, who never could cross the line, and for all the "boys from Peoplestown," who have crossed and will continue to do so.

THE HIDDEN CONTRIBUTORS

Seeking Truth in the Land
of the Free

Emerging nations do not usually have the resources to support extensive scientific establishments. And the United States in the Colonial and post-Revolutionary periods was no exception. The people who settled this land came here to hack a place for themselves out of the wilderness, and they just did not have time to be scientists or to care much about people who did. Many of the European settlers used black African slaves to help them build their places in the New World, and in so doing they set the stage for a conflict that would tear the young nation apart and bring about a lingering national tragedy.

It was not until well after the Civil War that the United States began to produce a scientific establishment equal in stature to the older scientific establishments in Europe. There were, of course, some pre-Civil War American scientists such as Benjamin Franklin, David Rittenhouse, Asa Gray, and Louis Agassiz. And among these early American scientific pioneers were men such as Benjamin Banneker and Norbert Rillieux who were descendants of black African slaves. Banneker wanted to be a pure scientist, seeking knowledge for its own sake, and Rillieux tried to apply scientific knowledge to the solution of practical problems. Both men experienced some triumph and more than their share of frustration in attempting to find truth in the land of the free.

CAN YOU DIRECT ME

TO BANNEKER SQUARE?

In the late seventeenth century, a young Englishwoman named Molly Welsh was accused of stealing a pail of milk. Despite her protestations that the cow had knocked over the pail, she was convicted and sentenced to be deported to the American Colonies. She was further sentenced to serve for seven years as an indentured servant to pay for her passage. If she had been able to pay the price of the milk, she would have been a free woman.

Molly Welsh's tragedy was all too common. At the time thousands of people were deported, imprisoned, or put to death for such minor things as stealing a pail of milk or for being in debt. These injustices were happening against the background of growing interest in science, literature, music, and political thought, which later historians were to call the "Age of Enlightenment."

When Molly Welsh was forced to leave England, Sir Isaac Newton had just published his laws of universal gravitation, and John Wallis had published his concepts of multi-dimensional geometry. But the work of men such as

Newton and Wallis did not immediately affect the life of Molly Welsh. Indeed, Molly was probably unaware of the existence of Newton, Wallis, and the other gentlemen who were causing the Enlightenment to happen. Such activity was only for the wealthy, titled, and privileged, who did not have to worry about the price of a pail of milk. It was only men such as these, free of the necessity of working for a living, who could be the "gentleman scientists" of the Enlightenment.

When Molly arrived in Maryland Colony she was bought for her seven years' service by a tobacco farmer. Many, if not most, of the early Colonial settlers came here in the same manner. Molly and the other indentured servants were more fortunate than the black slaves who were being brought here in growing numbers. At least Molly knew she would be free after seven years. The slaves had nothing to look forward to but a life little different from that of a horse.

The Declaration of Independence was based largely on the writings of Enlightenment philosophers, but most of the Enlightenment ideas, especially science, were slow to reach these shores. The thousands of people who came to America did so to escape some of the more unenlightened aspects of life in Europe. Many of them, such as slaves and indentured servants, did not come here willingly. They were torn from their homes and sent to an uncertain life in a land that was still, for the most part, wilderness. They were too immersed in the hard, brutal facts of making a living in this new land to have much time for scientific or other enlightening thoughts. And such was the case with the indentured servant and the black slave who were Benjamin Banneker's grandparents.

Through careful frugality during her years of service, Molly managed to save a small sum of money. When she had served her time, she bought a small piece of land in the Patapsco River valley near Baltimore. Molly worked the farm herself for a while, but the work was too much for one person. So, in 1692 she walked down to a harbor in Chesapeake Bay where a slave ship was anchored, and she bought two male slaves.

It was not at all unusual for ex-indentured servants to buy slaves; the acquisition of slaves was a step up the social ladder. Molly, however, did not keep her human status symbols. She freed the two slaves shortly after she bought them. Such manumissions were not too uncommon, but they usually occurred at the death of the master or when the master had acquired sufficient wealth to be able to afford such generosity. But, then again, one of Molly's slaves was not an ordinary kind of man.

It was apparent to all observers that the slave of Molly Welsh, who called himself Bannaka, possessed unusual intelligence and ability. He claimed to be the son of an African tribal King. His bearing was regal, his demeanor was proud and unsubmissive. Shortly after Bannaka was freed, Molly and Bannaka were married. Upon the marriage, Bannaka's name was Anglicized to Banneker, by which surname the couple was known.

In the early eighteenth century in America there were no laws against interracial marriages. Indeed, despite the existence of slavery, relationships between free blacks and whites were much more relaxed than was the case in later years. Marriages such as that of Molly and Bannaka were fairly common at the time and were generally accepted as being as natural as any other marriage. Most of the hard-working, individualistic colonists felt that the choice of marriage partners was the business only of the people involved.

The Bannekers prospered on their farm, which was known

to be one of the most efficiently run in the Patapsco valley. The Bannekers had four children. The oldest child, Mary, married a black man named Robert, who had been a slave on a nearby plantation and had converted to Christianity. (In the early days of slavery, some masters would free a slave who had accepted Christianity. The practice was later discontinued.) Since Robert had no last name, he assumed his wife's maiden name. Their first child and only son, Benjamin, was born in 1731.

Mary and Robert remained on her parents' farm until 1737, when they bought a piece of land not too far from that of the elder Bannekers. Robert Banneker amazed his neighbors with some very sophisticated farming methods. As far as is known, Robert Banneker was the first in the valley to employ irrigation as a means of increasing his crop yield. Apparently he had learned irrigation methods when he was a farmer on his tribal lands in Africa. The spring that supplied irrigation water was known for many years as "Bannaky Springs." It also supplied water for the elder Bannekers' farm. Robert and Mary produced good crops even when other farmers had lean years because of poor rainfall.

Young Benjamin's life seemed to be predetermined. It was logical to assume that he would inherit his father's farm and continue to live a farmer's life. At that, he was luckier than most black men in the Colonies. Even the relatively few black men who were free faced uncertain futures.

During Benjamin Banneker's lifetime there were few, if any, laws restricting the lives of black men. Free black men could vote, go where they pleased, and conduct their lives within the laws that applied to all men. But there were many non-legal restrictions, and these were ambiguous and capricious.

Although black and white men worked side by side in apparent harmony, a black man never knew what to expect from one day to the next. The status of the black man was particularly uncertain if he traveled from one place to another. Since the Colonies had a limited economy, it was difficult for free black men in cities to find good jobs. Most of them, therefore, lived in poverty or near poverty. So it would have been rather foolish for Banneker to leave the security of his family's prosperous farm for the uncertainties of life in cities such as Philadelphia or Boston.

It was soon evident that Benjamin was not like the other boys in the neighborhood. His grandmother, Molly, had taught him to read, and that ability alone set him apart from most of his neighbors, black or white. He was able to get some formal education at a Quaker school that was within walking distance of his home. It was fortunate that the school accepted all willing students regardless of color.

Benjamin attended school until he was fifteen. He exhibited a remarkable skill in mathematics. The school was limited in its offerings and according to accounts of people who knew him, Benjamin learned arithmetic only as far as the "double position." (The meaning of the term "double position" is not clear. It may have referred to complex fractions.) After he left school to help his father on the farm, Benjamin taught himself algebra and geometry.

He was a quiet boy and kept largely to himself. While other children did the sort of things most children do, Benjamin read every book he could find. Books of any description, however, were expensive and difficult to get, so his self-education did not follow any plan. Despite these difficulties, he accumulated quite a bit of general knowledge. He developed a particular interest in mathematics, astronomy, and other sciences. By the time he reached young adulthood Benjamin was, without doubt, the most learned man in the Patapsco valley.

The motivation to read and learn must have come from within Banneker's own mind. There was no one in the valley who could have encouraged him to study such things as advanced mathematics and astronomy. Advanced learning was not necessary for running a farm. His father and grandfather were both exceptionally intelligent men. Since they had been forced from Africa as slaves, they, of course, had had no opportunity for formal education. But Benjamin's parents and grandparents fostered a home atmosphere of learning and awareness, which certainly influenced the development of his love of gaining knowledge.

Actually, there was no one in the valley with whom Banneker could discuss what he had learned. It may have occurred to him to try to go to a university or college. But the very few institutions of higher learning that existed in the Colonies would not likely have accepted Banneker or any other black man.

There was very little scientific activity in the Colonies before the Revolution and for quite some time thereafter. The American people were too busy with the hard work of building a nation to bother with the time-consuming demands of scientific work. While many European governments supported science, there was no financial basis for such support in the Colonies and certainly no desire on the part of Congress after the Revolution. And, for the most part, the few people who were interested in scientific activity were scattered and disorganized.

What little science that existed was concentrated in the cities, especially Philadelphia. It was in Philadelphia that Benjamin Franklin conducted his electricity experiments. David Rittenhouse, the early American astronomer who made the first telescope in the United States, carried out his work in Philadelphia. The American Philosophical Society, one of the few successful early American scientific societies, was founded in Philadelphia. However, European scientists did not think that the work of American scientists, with the exception of Franklin, would ever be of any importance.

Franklin and Rittenhouse had other learned men with whom to share their ideas. And Franklin had opportunities to travel to Europe where the action in science was. In fact, Franklin held membership in many European scientific societies, such as the Royal Society of London. Banneker, however, was isolated, and he had to work on the farm. This limited the time he had for study to the winter months. Banneker had to depend on whatever happened to come his way. And one of the things that happened to come his way was a pocket watch.

A pocket watch is a thing most people would not find particularly inspiring, but it was the first watch Banneker had ever seen. He studied the workings of the watch and decided that he would make a clock, using the watch as a guide. Clocks were rare in the Colonies, and the few that were there had been imported from Europe or had been assembled from parts made in Europe. In the relatively remote Patapsco valley, the day's activities were timed by the sun, since no one owned a clock or a watch.

Banneker made his clock entirely from wood. The only tools he had were various knives for whittling the parts and a caliper for gauging the proportionally larger sizes of the clock parts. He started the job around 1758 and is known to have finished it in 1761. Banneker commented that the most difficult part of the job was to get the hour and minute hands to move in the proper relationship to each other. The gears had to be precisely cut and assembled in the proper balance. Although he did not know it, when he had finished, Banneker had constructed the first completely American-made clock.

The clock created quite a sensation in the valley and for many miles around. News of his clock spread, and it became somewhat of a tourist attraction. People traveled great distances to Banneker's cabin to see the wonderful clock and the remarkable man who had made it. It was reported in various newspapers and was cited years later as evidence that a black man could accomplish as much if not more than a white man could.

The clock made Banneker known outside his immediate area. But, still he lacked companions who could share his interests and level of achievement. Communication with other scientists is very important to a scientist. Without it there is no exchange of knowledge, and the individual interested in science cannot advance beyond the status of an amateur. Banneker had no contact with any of the fledgling American scientific societies. Scientific societies had been formed in Europe to improve communication among scientists. They also encouraged men of wealth and position to become supporting patrons of those scientists who did not have the means to support their work. In Europe, these patrons were usually kings, princes, or wealthy merchants. The young United States was notably lacking in people with the means or desire to be patrons of science.

After the death of his father in 1759, Banneker inherited the farm and found that he had even less time to devote to his scientific interests. He and his mother tried hiring tenant farmers, but Banneker was not much of a businessman. The tenants stole from him and he was too kind to call them to task for it. It is reported that he even watched as his tenants and some neighborhood boys stole the fruit from his trees, and he never said anything about it. Eventually, he had to dismiss the tenants and try once again to work the farm himself.

Banneker could have bought slaves had he been so inclined. There were many instances of free blacks buying slaves. But even though owning slaves would have enabled him to spend more time on his scientific work, slavery was against his principles, and he probably never entertained the possibility. Banneker never married and therefore had no children to help him on the farm. He may have thought that the responsibilities of a wife and children would distract him from his scientific work.

After he built his clock and word of his mathematical abilities got around, he began to receive many letters relating to mathematical problems. At the time, many of the more educated, wealthy gentry amused themselves with problems, since solving them was considered to be intellectually stimulating. There was very little entertainment such as theater and music. Visiting in each other's homes and in coffeehouses and inns was the chief diversion, and politics and mathematics were frequently the topics of discussion. In the upwardly mobile society of the Colonial and early national periods, evidence of learning and intellectual ability was as much a status symbol among the socially elite as money and land. And Benjamin Banneker's problem solutions helped many a wealthy planter get "one better" over a social rival.

One of Banneker's favorite activities was the writing of problems in verse. Writing poetry and devising mathematical problems are difficult enough in themselves. But combining poetry and mathematics requires great mastery of both language and mathematics. Banneker received many requests from the gentry for his mathematical poems. Only one of these problems has been preserved. And this one is known only due to the memory of one Charles W. Dorsey who knew Banneker and recited it, in 1845, to a Maryland historian who was looking for material on Banneker. It reads in part:

> . . . Make me a vessel if we can agree
> The top and the bottom diameter define
> To bear that proportion as fifteen to nine
> Thirty-five inches are just what I crave
> No more and no less in the depth will I have
> Just thirty-nine gallons this vessel must hold
> . . . Now my worthy friend find out if you can
> The vessel's dimensions and comfort the man!

The answer to this problem has been determined to be 24.746 inches in diameter at the top and 14.876 inches at the bottom.

Banneker's life underwent an unexpected change in 1772. In that year, the Ellicott family moved into the Patapsco valley. The Ellicotts were Quakers and members of one of the more prominent Maryland families. They were surveyors and they all had a keen interest in mathematical and scientific matters. Andrew Ellicott had a reputation as being one of the more prominent surveyors in the Colonies.

Surveyors were very important people at the time. As the country was settled there was great demand for their services in determining land boundaries and building roads and highways. Many indentured servants and other people who came here with nothing, advanced up the social and economic ladder by buying land with money earned from surveying. George Washington was a surveyor when he was a young man, and he also advanced his position with military service and by marrying a rich widow.

The Ellicotts had come to the valley to set up a flour mill. It did not take long for the Ellicotts and Banneker to seek each other out, and they became close friends. Joseph Ellicott and Banneker had much in common since Joseph had also made a clock. And the Ellicotts encouraged Banneker to expand the range of his scientific work.

When the Ellicotts set up their mill it seemed to the residents of the valley, Banneker included, that the enterprise was somewhat ill-advised. Most of the farmers raised tobacco rather than wheat. However, the Ellicotts assured the success of their enterprise by encouraging the farmers to switch to wheat. The reputations of the Ellicotts contributed to their persuasive powers, and they soon had a thriving business. The uncertain political situation also stimulated the change from tobacco to wheat. The possibility of separation from Britain was very real, and with that separation, the major market for tobacco would be cut off. At the same time, there was a good domestic market for flour. The mill became the focal point of the region and soon a village called Ellicott's Lower Mills grew in the area of the mill.

The setting up of the mill was a boon to Banneker in many ways. The Ellicotts and the mill employees purchased fruit and honey from the Banneker farm. The influx of people resulted in more sales and prosperity for Banneker and his mother. But the major benefit to Banneker was not the sale of more honey and fruit, but the Ellicotts, who were accomplished mathematicians and fairly active amateur astronomers. Banneker at last had the companionship of people who shared his interests and accomplishments.

As was the custom of the time, Banneker and the Ellicotts visited each other frequently. The Ellicotts were as fascinated with Banneker's clock as Banneker was with the mill machinery. The mill became a sort of informal gathering place for Banneker, the Ellicotts, and other interested villagers. The news-hungry village people hoped to pick up bits of information from the discussions of Banneker and the Ellicotts. George Ellicott traveled a great deal, and when he did he spoke of his accomplished black neighbor. Banneker soon found that his mail increased as more gentry requested mathematical problems and solutions.

Contact with the Ellicotts did indeed stimulate Banneker to do more scientific work. But the demands of the farm kept him from doing as much as he would have liked. Banneker was really not interested in farming. He farmed only because he had to do something for a living. He would have much preferred to spend his time on mathematical and astronomical studies, but science is not the kind of thing that lends itself to part-time efforts. Banneker determined to make himself a full-time scientist.

He discussed the problem with his friend George Ellicott, in 1783, and Ellicott agreed to buy Banneker's land. Banneker and Ellicott worked out a system of payments based on Banneker's estimate of how long he expected to live. Banneker, then age fifty-two, proposed that his land was worth £180 in the Maryland currency then in use. Guessing that he would live for another fifteen years, he asked to be paid £12 a year. They further agreed that Banneker would continue to live in the small cabin on the land. The estimate of how long he had to live was the most significant mathematical error Banneker ever made. Banneker lived eight years beyond the fifteen he had allocated to himself. Ellicott, however, continued to pay the £12 over Banneker's objections, soothing Banneker's feelings by insisting that the land increased in value.

Banneker now had a patron of sorts and a private income. Benjamin Banneker, the grandson of a slave and an indentured servant, was now a "gentleman scientist."

When Banneker sold his land it completely confounded his neighbors. They could not understand why a man would give up one of the best, if not the very best, farms in the entire Patapsco valley. Banneker now settled into a routine which scandalized the surrounding farmers. Every clear night he would leave his cabin with a blanket and notebooks. He would lie flat on his back looking at the stars until dawn, when he reluctantly returned to his cabin for sleep. Rising at noon, he would spend the rest of the day working on his calculations and correspondence.

To the good, hard-working, but not very bright neighbors, sleeping away half the day was nothing short of sinful. Many of the neighboring farmers had some very unkind things to say about this black man who neglected his farm. They could never begin to understand why a man would care to stay up all night just to look at the stars.

Banneker carried out his observations with only his eyes and brain as tools. Since he owned no books on astronomy and no instruments, the scope of his observations was severely limited. His situation changed dramatically in 1787 when George Ellicott gave him some astronomical books and instruments. The books were Mayer's *Astronomical Tables*, Ferguson's *Astronomy*, and Leadbeater's *Lunar Tables*. At the time these were considered to be the most reliable sources of astronomical information. He lost no time in getting to work, and he soon detected errors in Mayer's projection of a solar eclipse.

Banneker later did his own projection of the solar eclipse in question. An eclipse projection is an extremely intricate and complicated calculation. The ability to carry out this kind of calculation and to detect and correct an authoritative astronomer's error is the mark of a professional rather than an amateur.

With the aid of the books and instruments Banneker began to organize his observations into information which he would later incorporate into an almanac. The Ellicotts had encouraged Banneker to work on an almanac and had indicated that they would help him get a publisher. Almanacs were in very wide use at the time. Next to the Bible, an almanac was the book most likely to be found in American homes of the period. Farmers depended on them for planning their work. Almanacs contained the times of the rising and setting of the sun, moon, and planets. They also included weather predictions and little articles on various topics. They were the "poor man's encyclopedia."

Before he could do much work on his almanac, Banneker was thrust into more prominence than ever before by political manipulations of which he was unaware. When the Constitution was drawn up it was generally agreed that a permanent site for the nation's capital had to be chosen. Moving about from one place to another did little to enhance the shaky reputation of Congress. The "residence bill," establishing a permanent federal district, was finally passed in 1790. The bill did not specify the location, but left it to the President to make a choice. Although George Washington was the President, the choice of site was actually the result of a political compromise between Thomas Jefferson and Alexander Hamilton.

Hamilton was generally recognized as the spokesman of the North, for strong central government; Jefferson upheld the southern view of more powers for the individual states. The capital city compromise was effected when Hamilton agreed to get northern support for a southern capital city if Jefferson would encourage Southerners to support the Fed-

eral assumption of state debts, a measure which served to
strengthen the central government.

The chosen site for the "Grand Columbian Federal City"
was a ten-mile square of land on the Potomac River near
the town of Georgetown, about forty miles from where
Banneker lived. To plan the city, President Washington appointed a "Board of Commissioners." Chosen to do the
actual planning was the engineer and architect, Major
Pierre Charles L'Enfant, who had come to the United States
from France as a volunteer during the Revolutionary War.

L'Enfant had grand visions for the Federal City. He saw
it as a city of broad sweeping boulevards and magnificent
public buildings. His plan, which included boulevards
radiating out from central points like spokes of a wheel, was
similar to Versailles, Rome, and other European cities.
L'Enfant did not concern himself too much with such details
as where people were going to live in this grand city, or
with necessary services for the population. Although he
changed his mind often, he fiercely defended his ideas for
the moment that he had them. Resisting all suggestions from
anyone other than himself, he was very difficult to work
with.

One of the terms of L'Enfant's commission was that he
was to produce an engraved map of the proposed city. This
was very important politically. The Congressmen who were
voting the money wanted to be assured that the money was
for something real and not imagined. Despite much prod-
ding L'Enfant failed to produce the map, and as time went
on, Washington and Jefferson were afraid that Congress
might scuttle the whole business.

Jefferson tactfully suggested to L'Enfant that a surveyor
be appointed to assist him. At Jefferson's suggestion, Washington appointed Andrew Ellicott for the job. Upon accept-

ing the appointment, Ellicott asked Banneker to be his assistant. Banneker accepted and Ellicott relayed the information to Jefferson. The official appointment was made by President Washington. Thus Benjamin Banneker became the first black presidential appointee in the United States.

The Georgetown *Weekly Ledger* of March 12, 1791, reported that Andrew Ellicott had arrived in Georgetown "attended by Benjamin Banneker, an Ethiopian, whose abilities as surveyor and astronomer already prove that Mr. Jefferson's concluding that that race of men were void of mental endowment was without foundation." Jefferson had previously made statements about the inferiority of blacks in a series of essays called *Notes on Virginia.*

Banneker by this time was fairly well known as an accomplished mathematician and as the amazing "Afro-American Astronomer." This was not enough to overcome the prejudices of some of the commissioners who voiced objections to eating at the same table with him. Despite these objections, Banneker was invited to dine with the commissioners. Banneker was a gentle, non-aggressive man, and in order not to expose himself and Ellicott to unpleasant incidents at the dining table he refused the invitation. Banneker finally agreed to eat in the same room with the commissioners but at a separate table. It is almost inconceivable that men who were intelligent enough to serve on a commission charged with planning a national capital city could make such an issue over who was and who was not to sit at an eating table.

L'Enfant objected to everybody, regardless of race, color, or creed. His cooperation with Ellicott and Banneker was grudging and reluctant, when there was any cooperation at all. The site swarmed with land speculators who were trying to buy up lots even before the streets had been laid out and the location of the lots determined. When a politically important person started to erect a house in the middle of where New Jersey Avenue was supposed to be, L'Enfant flew into a rage and had the house torn down. Washington had no choice but to dismiss L'Enfant. L'Enfant left in an understandable huff and took his plans with him.

The commissioners were left with ten square miles of mud, buildings in various stages of non-completion, and curious tracks in the mud which were supposed to be avenues and grand boulevards. And they had no plans with which to bring some kind of order out of the muddy chaos.

Banneker amazed Ellicott and the commissioners by reproducing L'Enfant's plans almost exactly as the volatile Frenchman had drawn them. While working on the surveying job Banneker had written down L'Enfant's field notes and used them for practice in map making. His constant efforts to improve his skills had resulted in the saving of Washington City. It is entirely possible that Congress might have withdrawn its support if the commissioners had not been able to present the plans and maps.

It did not take long, however, for Banneker and Ellicott to become disgusted with the politicians and speculators, who knowingly or not obstructed the project. In time, they followed the example of L'Enfant and left the project— but not before Banneker had become known throughout the new nation as the "Afro-American Astronomer" who had helped to build the city of Washington in the District of Columbia.

Banneker's important contributions have only recently been recognized by the District of Columbia with the designation of a new school as Benjamin Banneker Junior High School. There was never before a street, park, or public square named in honor of Benjamin Banneker.

Banneker returned to his home in the middle of 1791. He was now quite a celebrity and the neighbors who had previously ridiculed him for sleeping until noon now eagerly sought him out to hear of his experiences in Washington. Banneker traveled about the countryside on horseback relating the exciting events to the news-hungry, isolated farmers.

During the Washington project, Banneker had devoted his leisure time to his almanac. By the time he left Washington his first almanac was almost complete, and he finished it in the summer of 1791. The Ellicotts contacted James McHenry (Fort McHenry of "Star Spangled Banner" fame was named after a member of this family), a prominent member of one of Maryland's first families, who was later to serve as Secretary of War under President Adams. McHenry brought the almanac to the attention of the Baltimore publishing firm of Goddard and Angel. In a letter to Goddard and Angel, McHenry wrote:

> . . . I consider this Negro as fresh proof that the powers of the mind are disconnected with the color of the skin, or, in other words, a striking contrast to Hume's doctrine, that "the Negroes are naturally inferior to the whites and unsusceptible of attainments in arts and sciences." In every civilized country we shall find thousands of white liberally educated and who have enjoyed greater opportunities for instruction than this Negro, his inferiors in those intellectual acquirements and capacities that form the most characteristic features in the human race . . .

The "Hume" mentioned in the letter had written some essays on the alleged "intellectual inferiority" of Africans.

Goddard and Angel agreed to publish Banneker's almanac, and it first appeared in 1792. Goddard and Angel hoped to make money from the almanac and they did. But they had another purpose in publishing the work which they expressed in the preface to the 1792 edition. They wrote in the flowery language of the time:

> We are gratified in representing a complete and accurate Ephemeris for the year 1792, calculated by a sable descendent of Africa, who by this specimen of ingenuity evinces to demonstrate that mental powers and endowments are not exclusive excellence of white people, but that the rays of science may alike illume the mind of men of every clime however they may differ in the color of their skin . . .

Banneker's first almanac also contained a foreword that had been written by McHenry in a letter to Goddard and Angel.

> It is about three years since Mr. George Ellicott lent his Mayer's *Tables,* Ferguson's *Astronomy,* Leadbeater's *Lunar Tables* and some astronomical instruments, but without accompanying them with either hint or instruction, that might further his studies or lead him to apply them to any useful result. These books and instruments, the first of the kind he had ever seen, opened a new world to Benjamin, and from thence forward has employed his leisure in astronomical researches.

The almanacs sold rather well, not only in Maryland but in all of the Middle Atlantic States. There were items about him in newspapers all over the country. His accomplishments even inspired a Miss Mason to poetry. It was a long poem, which included the following:

> . . . But thou a man exalted high
> Conspicuous in the world's keen eye
> On record now, thy names enrolled,
> And future ages will be told
> There lived a man named BANNEKER
> An African Astronomer!

Although it was not particularly prize-winning poetry, the Mason poem was indicative of the attention Banneker received after his almanac was published.

As the result of his work on the District of Columbia project and his almanacs, Banneker had achieved no small degree of fame in the young nation. Not only was he free to engage in whatever scientific work he wished, but that work was also bringing him a modest income from the sale of his almanacs. By all accounts he should have been a happy man. Yet there was much that disturbed him and kept him far from being happy.

There were many signs that blacks and whites in the United States were being drawn into a national tragedy. Banneker and other black men had had great hopes when the Colonies separated from Great Britain. The words of the Declaration of Independence had promised a new life of freedom for all citizens.

Black men had fought in the Revolution, but for a time, George Washington had yielded to the demands of slave holders and had halted Negro enlistments. Only the offer of the British to grant freedom to any slave who would join the British Army induced the Colonial Army to again accept black men.

The winning of the Revolution and the gaining of independence for the United States had done little to improve the lot of the black man. In point of fact, with the coming of independence the lives of blacks became progressively worse. Most of the northern states did away with slavery after the war, but as they did, laws were passed which severely restricted black men. Blacks were forbidden to vote, go to public schools, and to use public transportation. Slavery remained in the South, and it gained strength as cotton and sugar cultivation proved to be profitable.

Benjamin Bannaker's

PENNSYLVANIA, DELAWARE, MARY-

LAND, AND VIRGINIA

ALMANAC,

FOR THE

YEAR of our LORD 1795;

Being the Third after Leap-Year.

PHILADELPHIA:

Printed for WILLIAM GIBBONS, Cherry Street

Title page of 1795 edition of Benjamin Banneker's almanac.
(*Courtesy of New York Public Library*)

In an attempt to rationalize slavery, the pro-slavery men promoted the widely believed fallacy that black men were naturally inferior to whites and were better off as slaves under the "protective" care of their white masters. Even those who did not care about slavery, or were opposed to it, held to the idea that black men were inferior and should be held in check by laws.

Thomas Jefferson, who had been instrumental in getting Banneker appointed to the District of Columbia Commission and had written the words "all men are created equal," had also written in his *Notes on Virginia* statements about the inferiority of black men. Jefferson continued to hold slaves on his Monticello plantation.

The promise of a free, productive society for all men, which Benjamin Banneker seemed to symbolize, was rapidly fading as the wall between black and white rose higher and stronger. Banneker could not sit silently as did many of his black brothers. He had to do something about the growing tragedy of the black man in America. He took it upon himself to write to no less a personage than Thomas Jefferson. He sent the letter just before his almanac was published and included the manuscript with his letter.

Maryland, Baltimore Country,
August 19, 1791

Sir,

I am fully sensible of the greatness of the freedom I take with you on the present occasion; a liberty which seemed to me scarcely allowable, when I reflected on that distinguished and dignified station in which you stand, and the almost general prejudice and prepossession, which is so prevalent in the world against those of my complexion.

I suppose it is a truth too well attested to you, to need

a proof here, that we are a race of beings, who have long laboured under the abuse and censure of the world; that we have long been looked upon with an eye of contempt; and that we have long been considered rather as brutish than human, and scarcely capable of mental endowments.

Sir, I hope I may safely admit, in consequence of the report which has reached me, that you a man less inflexible in sentiments of this nature, than many others; that you are measurably friendly, and well disposed towards us; and that you are willing and ready to lend your aid and assistance to our relief, from those many distresses, and numerous calamities, to which we are reduced.

Now, Sir, if this is founded in truth, I apprehend you will embrace every opportunity, to eradicate that train of absurd and false ideas and opinions, which so generally prevail with respect to us; and that your sentiments are concurrent with mine, which are, that one universal Father hath given being to us all; . . . and endowed us all with the same faculties; and that however variable we may be in society or religion, however diversified in situation or colour, we are all of the same family, and stand in the same relation to Him . . .

Sir, I freely and cheerfully acknowledge, that I am of the African race, and in that colour which is natural to them, of the deepest dye; and it is under a sense of the most profound gratitude to the Supreme Ruler of the Universe, that I now confess to you, that I am not under that state of tyrannical thralldom, and inhuman captivity, to which too many of my brethren are doomed, but that I have abundantly tasted to the fruition of those blessings, which proceeded from that free and unequalled liberty with which you are favoured . . .

Sir, suffer me to recall to your mind that time, in which the arms and tyranny of the British crown were exerted, with every powerful effort, in order to reduce you to a state of servitude; look back, I entreat you, on the variety of dangers to which you were opposed; reflect on that time, in which every human aid appeared unavailable . . . and you cannot but be led to a serious and grateful sense of your miraculous and providential preservation . . .

This, Sir, was a time when you clearly saw into the injustice of a state of slavery, and in which you had just apprehensions of the horrors of its condition. It was then that your abhorrence thereof was so excited that you publicly held forth this true and invaluable doctrine; which is worthy to be recorded and remembered in all succeeding ages: "We hold these truths to be self-evident, that all men are created equal; that they are endowed by their Creator with certain inalienable rights, and that among these are life, liberty, and the pursuit of happiness."

Here was a time, in which your tender feelings for yourselves had engaged you thus to declare; you were then impressed with proper ideas of the great violation of liberty, and the free possession of those blessings, to which you were entitled by nature, but sir, how pitiable it is to reflect, that although you were so fully convinced of the benevolence of the Father of Mankind, and of His equal and impartial distribution of these rights and privileges, which He hath conferred upon them, that you should at the same time counteract His mercies, in detaining by fraud and violence, so numerous a part of my brethren under groaning captivity, and cruel oppression, that you should at the same time be found guilty of that most criminal act, which you professedly detested in others, with respect to yourselves.

And now, Sir, although my sympathy and affection for my brethren has caused my enlargement thus far, I ardently hope that your candour and generosity will plead with you in my behalf, when I make known to you that it was not originally my design; but having taken up my pen in order to direct to you, as a present, a copy of an Almanac which I have calculated for the succeeding year, I was unexpectedly and unavoidably led thereto.

This calculation is the product of my arduous study, in this my advanced stage of life . . . I have taken the liberty to direct a copy to you which I humbly request you will favourably receive and although you may have the opportunity of perusing it after its publication, yet I desire to send it to you in manuscript previous thereto, thereby you might not only have an earlier inspection, but that you might also view it in my own handwriting.

And now, Sir, I shall conclude, and subscribe myself, with the most profound respect.

> Your most obedient humble servant,
> Benjamin Banneker

Jefferson read the letter and honored Banneker with a prompt reply.

Philadelphia, Aug. 30, 1791

Sir,

I thank you most sincerely, for your letter of the 19th instant, and for the Almanac it contained. Nobody wishes more than I do, to see such proofs as you exhibit, that nature has given to our black brethren talents equal to those of the other color of men; and that the appearance of the want of them is owing merely to the degraded condition of their existence, both in Africa and America. I can add with truth, that nobody wishes more ardently to see a good system commenced, for raising the condition, both of their body and mind, to what it ought to be, as far as the imbecility of their present existence, and other circumstances, which cannot be neglected, will admit.

I have taken the liberty of sending your Almanac to Monsieur de Condorcet, Secretary of the Academy of Sciences, at Paris, and Member of the Philanthropic

Society, because I considered it as a document to which your whole colour have a right for their justification against the doubts which have been entertained of them.

> I am, with great esteem, Sir,
> Your most obedient humble servant,
> Tho. Jefferson

Apparently, Jefferson had been quite moved by Banneker's plea, for, in a letter Jefferson wrote to the Marquis de Condorcet, he expressed an attitude much changed from what he had written in *Notes on Virginia*.

I am happy to be able to inform you that we have now in the United States a Negro, the son of a black man born in Africa and of a black woman born in the United States, who is a very respectable mathematician. I procured him to be employed under one of our chief directors in laying out of the new federal city on the Potomac, & in the interval of his leisure while on the work, he made an Almanac for the next year, which he sent me in his own handwriting, & which I am enclosing to you. I have seen very elegant solutions of Geometrical problems by him. Add to this that he is a worthy and respectable member of society. He is a free man. I shall be delighted, to see these instances of moral eminence so multiplied as to prove that the want of talents observed in them is merely the effect of their degraded condition and not proceeding from any difference in the stature of the parts on which intellect depends.

Jefferson wrote to Condorcet as an official of one of the most influential scientific societies in the world. Condorcet was also active in anti-slavery movements and was a member of the *Société des Amis des Noirs* (Society of Friends of the Blacks). Jefferson, no doubt, thought that Condorcet would be happy to hear of Banneker as living evidence that intelligence was not a function of the lack of skin color.

Jefferson was probably happy enough to be able to report to Condorcet that the young United States had scientists of any color other than the well-known Benjamin Franklin. It is unfortunate that Banneker was not invited to join or participate in some way in the activities of the American Philosophical Society or one of the other scientific societies that were trying to survive in the new nation. If Banneker's skin color had not prevented him from entering the main stream of scientific thought in America, Jefferson may well have had more to report to Condorcet about the state of American science and Banneker's contributions to it.

Banneker made up an almanac every year, although they were no longer published after 1797. He was a familiar figure as he made the rounds of friends and neighbors in the Patapsco valley. By the time he had become well known, he was advanced in years, with white hair and tending to fat around the middle. Many of his neighbors commented that he looked somewhat like Benjamin Franklin.

He did not limit his work to mathematics and astronomy. He wrote a dissertation on bees and carried out a study of the seventeen-year locust. He was one of the first investigators to determine the seventeen-year periodicity of these insects. Even in his old age, Banneker was a keen observer of natural phenomena. In 1797 he wrote, "Standing at my door I heard the discharge of a gun, and in four or five seconds after the discharge, the small shot came rattling around me, one or two of which struck the house; Which plainly demonstrates that the velocity of sound is greater than that of a cannon bullet."

Banneker was also keenly interested in world affairs. He was especially concerned that war seemed to be the only way nations could settle differences. In one of his almanacs he included an essay, "A Lasting Peace," in which he made proposals that anticipated organizations such as the United Nations.

It was Banneker's habit to walk through the woods near his home, observing nature as he went. On an October morning in 1806 he started on one of these walks but collapsed before he had gone very far. Some friends and neighbors carried him back to his cabin where he died as his clock continued to tick away the minutes and hours.

An obituary in *The Federal Gazette and Baltimore Daily Advertiser* of October 28, 1806, praised him in eulogy and was, in effect, a summary of his life. Appearing in a slave state newspaper, an optimistic person might have thought it to be an indication that the determined rush into racial tragedy in the United States had been reversed.

On the day Banneker was buried, while the burial service was in progress, Benjamin Banneker's cabin burned to the ground. Most of his papers and his clock were destroyed. Fortunately, some of his papers had been left with the Ellicotts and other friends. Since almost everyone around Ellicotts Lower Mills was at the burial service, the fire had not been seen in time to put it out. The fire may have been started by some spiteful person who wanted to erase all evidence that a black man could be what Benjamin Banneker had been. If indeed the fire was deliberately started, the flames were only a foretaste of the tragedy that would tear the nation apart some fifty-five years later and carry the American people to the very real threat of more violence in the next century.

Three years after Benjamin Banneker died, the Maryland Legislature passed a law that took away the vote from all black men.

MAKE MY LIVING IN CANDY LAND

When Benjamin Banneker died in 1806 slavery was well established in the southern states. By that time, slavery had been abolished in most of the northern states, mainly because it was not profitable in the emerging factory system of the North. In the agricultural South, the labor of black slaves was eminently profitable to the owners, especially in the cultivation of two money crops—cotton and sugar. The profits gained from cotton and sugar soon killed the few southern emancipation efforts that had gained some momentum during and shortly after the Revolution. The physical work involved in growing cotton and sugar cane was so hard that free labor could not be obtained at wages low enough to enable the planters to compete in the world market.

The future of cotton had been assured by the invention of the cotton gin by the Yankee, Eli Whitney. (There is some evidence, impossible to substantiate, that Whitney got the idea for the cotton gin from a slave in Georgia, who had previously made a similar device.) The future of the sugar industry would be fortified by the invention of a black man born on a sugar plantation in the same year that Banneker died. This device, which would dramatically increase the sugar-producing capacities of cane plantations and consequently increase the demand for slaves, was invented by a man who was himself the son of a slave.

The record of his birth still exists in New Orleans: "Norbert Rillieux, quadroon *libre*, natural son of Vincent Rillieux and Constance Vivant, born March 17, 1806, baptized in St. Louis Cathedral by Pere Totoine." Vincent Rillieux was the wealthy owner of a large sugar cane plantation and Constance Vivant was his slave. In New Orleans, the word "quadroon" was used to describe anyone of mixed black and white ancestry. It did not necessarily mean "quarter black" as it did elsewhere. *Libre* indicated that the child's father had chosen to make him free.

Births resulting from the union of master and slave were quite common on southern plantations. But the acknowledgment of the birth by the father was not so common. In most cases, the father took no particular notice of the child, who was just another slave. But in some parts of the South, such children were made house servants. Indeed, many slaveowners would have as house servants only their own children born of slave mothers.

A plantation owner giving his name to his illegitimate child born of his black mistress would have caused quite a bit of adverse comment in most of the South except in New Orleans. The New Orleans society was unique in the United States, and well it might have been, for New Orleans had been part of the United States only three years when Norbert Rillieux was born. Before that time it had been alternately French and Spanish, and had evolved into one of the most exciting and culturally rich societies in the Western Hemisphere, if not the entire world.

Norbert Rillieux. (*Courtesy of Lloyd Douglas*)

Most of the people in New Orleans were of French origin. Spaniards comprised a fair-sized minority. The descendants of the original settlers were called Creoles. Numbers notwithstanding, the Creole influence in New Orleans was most evident. There were also large numbers of slaves in New Orleans. Although the lives of slaves were severely restricted by the harsh provisions of the *Code Noir*, the generally liberal attitude of the French settlers resulted in a much higher rate of manumissions than was the case in most of the United States. These manumitted slaves and their descendants comprised a large segment of the population.

Black people of mixed French and/or Spanish ancestry considered themselves to be Creoles, even though most of the white Creoles did not share this attitude. The black Creoles generally held themselves aloof from the other blacks and thought themselves superior since many of them were descended from some of the more distinguished French families. They were referred to as *Cordons Bleus,* an allusion to a blue cord or sash which had indicated position and importance in pre-Revolutionary France. Norbert Rillieux, as the son of a French planter and his favorite black mistress, qualified as a *Cordons Bleu.*

There was little if any social contact between the various New Orleans ethnic groups. Business, however, was another matter, and many of the *Cordons Bleus* became quite wealthy from engaging in the active New Orleans commerce. They developed a society and culture that included plantation owners, merchants, skilled artisans, poets, and musicians. Many were patrons of the arts, and sections of the New Orleans opera houses were reserved exclusively for their use. The New Orleans "liberal" attitude did not go so far as to permit open seating for blacks in theaters. Many *Cordons Bleus* owned slaves, and the sight of black men at slave markets, in the cutaway coats and high hats of the New Orleans gentry, bidding for black slaves, was a common one. After New Orleans became part of the United States the number of blacks who owned slaves declined, although as late as 1830 there were some 750 black slaveowners in New Orleans, most of whom were *Cordons Bleus.*

When, as a result of the 1803 Louisiana Purchase, New Orleans became part of the United States the situation of the black population began to change for the worse. These changes occurred in spite of a clause in the Purchase Treaty stipulating that the United States was to grant full citizenship to all free persons. As more poor-white Southerners poured into Louisiana, their attitudes became part of the scene, and on the eve of secession the lot of the *Cordons Bleus* and other free blacks was little different from the rest of the South.

The Americans or "Anglos" were socially spurned by the more-established residents. Patterns of social and residential separation were strengthened. There was a saying that a Creole could more easily travel to Paris than he could cross Canal Street into the "Anglo" areas.

Most of the Louisiana fortunes, including that of Vincent Rillieux, were built on sugar and on the backs of the slaves who labored in the cane fields. Young Norbert, who could have been a slave at the whim of his father, grew up with all the privileges attendant to the favorite son of a wealthy planter. Norbert may not have been the only illegitimate son fathered by Vincent Rillieux, but the relationship between Vincent Rillieux and Constance Vivant was not the casual sort of sexual liaison between master and slave girl that was all too prevalent on southern plantations. They were man and wife, in spirit if not legally, and they were extremely devoted to each other and to their son. The relationship between Vincent and Constance was not at all unique in the New Orleans culture. Many planters had favorite black mistresses whom they chose from among the slaves on their plantations or bought at the docket. And many of their children, such as Norbert Rillieux, numbered among the more distinguished of the *Cordons Bleus*.

Norbert's education, which included Catholic schools and tutors, followed the pattern of other sons of wealthy planters. He was given every cultural and material advantage. As the favorite son, Norbert did not have to take part in the work of the plantation. He was, however, very interested in plantation activities, and his observations certainly contributed to the ideas that later resulted in the invention for which he is known. Norbert was impressed by the brutally hard work and inefficient methods that went into the production of sugar.

The French settlers found that the rich soil of the Mississippi River delta plain and the long Louisiana summers were admirably suited to the cultivation of the tall sugar cane plants. The plants, which grow much higher than a man, are grown only for the juice in the long stems. The harvesting of sugar cane was, and still is, one of the most difficult and back-breaking jobs in all of agriculture. In slavery days, field hands strong enough to work in the cane fields were so much in demand that, at times, their price rose to as much as five thousand dollars. In order to get the maximum juice out of each plant, the stem is cut as close to the ground as possible. This necessitated a constant uncomfortable, bent-over position. Overseers on horseback rode herd on the slaves to see that they "got their back into it." The work of the slaves was by no means finished when the cane was cut. There was still much work ahead in crushing the juice out of the cane and turning the juice into sugar.

The juice was heated in a series of open kettles and pans called the "Jamaica Train." The various heating containers were referred to by French names such as *grande, flambeau, sirop,* and *batterie.* Gangs of slaves stood alongside the kettles and pans and poured the juice from one container to another with long-handled ladles. As the juice was passed along in the series it became thicker. In the last and smallest pan it was heated to crystallization, and various impurities were brought to the surface by applications of lime.

In addition to being inefficient the "Jamaica Train" was very hard and hot work for the sweating slaves who had to stand close by the steaming kettles. Accidents were frequent and many slaves bore disfiguring scars from scaldings by hot cane juice. Occasionally, the kettles would tip over or slaves might fall into them.

The quality of the sugar produced in the "Jamaica Train" could not be well controlled. Frequently it was dark and resembled molasses more than sugar. Much of the difficulty lay in determining just when to transfer the juice to the next container in the series. This was determined by eye and "feel" and various other factors based on experience and folklore. Norbert Rillieux became aware of the need for a more efficient way to produce sugar as he watched the slaves sweating over the kettles season after season. Whether his concern was over the slaves' plight or the desire for more profits is difficult to say. In this case a more profitable process resulted in an easier time for the slaves.

As Norbert approached the end of his precollege education, he developed an interest in engineering. Much of this interest came from his father, whose many efficiency-improving projects about the plantation gave him the status of an amateur engineer. There was never any doubt that Norbert would attend a French university. That sons of Creoles attended French schools was an established tradition. In Norbert's case, it was mandatory as well as traditional. There was no college in the United States that would have accepted Norbert Rillieux, *Cordons Bleu,* or not.

Rillieux studied at L'Ecole Central in Paris. Majoring in engineering, he was an outstanding student. At the time, the various specialties of engineering, such as chemical or mechanical, were not as sharply delineated as they are today. A student of engineering would apply his knowledge and talents to any number of projects that attracted his interest. Steam was rapidly bringing about many significant economic and social changes, which historians of later years would call the Industrial Revolution.

In 1830, shortly after he graduated, Rillieux was invited to become a member of the faculty of L'Ecole Central. At twenty-four he was the youngest instructor ever to be employed at the school. He was not an idle instructor. Soon after his appointment he published a series of papers on steam engines and steam economy. Steam engines of the period wasted more steam than they used, and much of the effort of engineers was directed at improving the efficiency of these engines.

Rillieux never forgot the sight of the slaves on his father's plantation laboring over the steaming kettles of the "Jamaica Train." He conceived of an idea that would put the steam to better use than making slaves sweat. Rillieux felt that heating the juice in open kettles wasted fuel. The principle that the boiling point of liquids is reduced as the atmospheric pressure is reduced had been established. Rillieux, therefore, proposed that if the cane juice was heated in a partial vacuum in a closed container, it would boil at a lower temperature with a consequent saving of fuel. This idea did not originate with Rillieux, but he carried the concept several steps further. He saw that the steam from one vessel could be used to heat the juice in the next vessel in the series. The device he formulated in his mind consisted of several enclosed vacuum pans connected by pipes that led the juice and steam from one container to the next.

Rillieux called his device the *multiple effect vacuum pan evaporator,* and he worked on the theory and practice of his evaporator several years before he returned to New Orleans where he hoped to get a patent and start the manufacture and sale of his invention to the New Orleans sugar planters.

The young engineer found a much changed New Orleans when he returned. If he had not had his father's plantation to which to return, he would have had trouble finding a place to sleep. Laws had been passed forbidding blacks to stay in most inns and hotels. Such laws had never existed during French rule or even during the most repressive years of Spanish rule. Rillieux did, however, succeed in obtaining Patent No. 3237, dated August 26, 1843.

If Rillieux's father had not chosen to make him free, Rillieux might have been unable to obtain a patent, even if by some miracle he, as a slave, had been able to obtain the necessary training in engineering. A few years after Rillieux obtained his patent, an Attorney General of the United States issued a ruling to the effect that slaves could not take out patents. He reasoned that slaves were property and that a piece of property could not obtain a patent. Inventions of slaves were ruled to be as much the property of the master as any other product of the slave's labor. One of Jefferson Davis' slaves had invented an improved ship propeller. Davis attempted to obtain a patent on behalf of his slave, and he was denied. When Davis was later President of the Confederacy, he suggested a clause in the Confederate Constitution stipulating that masters could take out patents for any inventions of their slaves.

After he returned to New Orleans Rillieux was offered a job as chief engineer at a sugar factory. He eagerly accepted the job, hoping that he would have an opportunity to manufacture a prototype of his invention and test it at the factory. This did not happen. An argument with the owner of the factory resulted in Rillieux leaving his job only shortly after he had accepted it.

He then made arrangements with a plantation owner named Zenon Ramon, who agreed to help Rillieux construct one of the evaporators on his plantation. The prototype was quickly constructed, but it did not perform well. The evaporator frequently broke down, and when it did work the rate of production was slow and the quality of the sugar was little better than the "Jamaica Train." There were many problems with Rillieux's original design, but the principle was sound and Rillieux was encouraged to make modifications.

In developing the evaporator Rillieux was a pioneer chemical engineer. The chemical engineer is concerned with taking principles developed in the chemical laboratory and devising machines that manufacture useful products on a large scale. The monstrous evaporators and catalytic crackers that produce gasoline and other petroleum products are among the more spectacular examples of the chemical engineer's craft. They operate on somewhat the same principles as Rillieux's multiple effect evaporator. In Rillieux's time, the basic principles of thermodynamics on which the operation of such devices are based were generally unknown. Rillieux actually applied these principles without realizing he was doing so.

(RIGHT)
Rillieux's second version of the evaporator. (*Courtesy of United States Department of Commerce*)

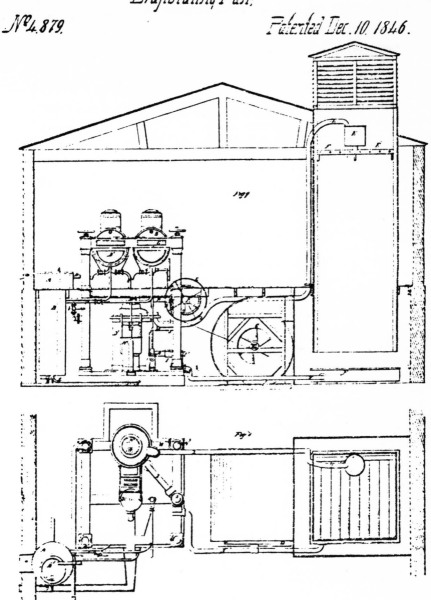

N. Rillieux.

Evaporating Pan.

Nº 4.879.

Patented Dec. 10. 1846.

For Rillieux, much encouragement and support came from another planter, Theodore Packwood. Work on the new version of the evaporator was carried out on the Packwood plantation. By 1845 Rillieux had constructed a new evaporator, and it was fully operational. The modified machine worked very well. It turned out a high quality product faster and more efficiently than ever before. And Theodore Packwood's slaves no longer had to sweat over steaming kettles of hot cane juice.

Rillieux obtained a patent on the improved evaporator in 1846. In his patent application he described the device as follows:

> . . . the first improvement is in the manner of connecting a steam engine with the evaporating pan or pans in such a manner that the engine shall be operated by the steam in its passage to the evaporating pan or pans, and the flow of steam so regulated by a weighted or other valve as to reach the said pan or pans at the temperature required for the process . . .

Rillieux, as many other inventors at the time, had to fight off a veritable army of imitators and patent pirates.

Diagram of front view of a Rillieux evaporator. (*Courtesy of Sugar y Azucar*)

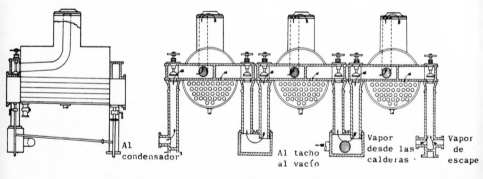

A mechanic named Stackhouse stole a set of Rillieux's plans and sent them to an accomplice in Germany. The operation of Rillieux's evaporator was not understood by the pirates, and the one they built did not work as efficiently as the units Rillieux built in the United States. The mistake persisted, however, and the pirated, inferior evaporators were used for years in many parts of the world.

Rillieux's invention was a formidable-looking apparatus. In a periodical magazine of the time it was described as being "composed of three or four cylindrical pans . . . arranged parallel to each other and supported on cast iron columns . . . A dome surmounts each pan, which makes the evaporator look like a locomotive."

Rillieux's evaporator was soon in demand, and it was installed on plantations in Louisiana and in the West Indies. The effect it had on the sugar industry was nothing short of revolutionary. Sugar production was dramatically increased. Rillieux's invention literally put sugar on the table of almost every American home. Before Rillieux, white, crystalline sugar was a relative luxury used on special occasions by people who could afford it. Most people used molasses or honey as sweeteners. The evaporator increased sugar production to the point where it became cheap and abundant, and the producers had to create new markets for it. Crystalline sugar soon became the common household item that it is today.

Although Rillieux's invention put the "Jamaica Train" in the museum and made the job of sugar refining easier for slaves, it had the effect of increasing the demand for slaves. Since the evaporator could process thousands of times more sugar than the "Jamaica Train," the planters felt a need to acquire more slaves to grow more cane. The labor in the cane fields was no less back breaking than it had been before.

The invention brought Rillieux a fair income and he was held in general praise by the leaders of the sugar industry. Yet, life in New Orleans was becoming more and more unbearable for Rillieux and other black men. The discriminatory lodging laws were only the first of a series of oppressive measures directed against black people. They were disenfranchised and denied entrance to theaters and other public places that had been open to them in the days of French rule. Louisiana, as the rest of the South, was consumed in the sectional crisis over slavery. Any statement or deed that, in the judgment of the pro-slavery forces, remotely strengthened the position of the abolitionists, was fiercely denounced.

Black battalions had contributed significantly to the American victory at the Battle of New Orleans in the War of 1812. But when Rillieux returned to New Orleans from Paris he found that black veterans of this battle were forbidden to take part in the annual Victory Day celebrations. The slaveholders feared that such acknowledgment of the blacks' role in American history would help the cause of the abolitionists.

Rillieux continued to try to participate in the social and commercial life of the city. He turned his attention to a problem of civil engineering: sewage disposal. The disposal of sewage had always been a serious problem in low-lying, marshy, New Orleans. Drainage was poor and the danger of epidemics was always present. Rillieux developed a plan that centered about a series of canals. Rillieux's plan would have been very beneficial to the general health of the city, but the city fathers refused to consider a plan submitted by a black man. Such an action would

A modern vacuum pan evaporator installation in Sweden. (*Courtesy of Kockum-Landsverk Landskrona, Sweden*)

have indeed given the abolitionists something to shout about. Many years later, however, New Orleans adopted a sewage disposal plan similar to Rillieux's.

Despite almost daily humiliations and frustrations, Rillieux remained in New Orleans. Then in 1854 a law was passed that required all blacks to carry an identification pass. This was too much for Rillieux. He left the city of his birth and returned to Paris. Many more *Cordons Bleus* and other New Orleans blacks followed his example.

Rillieux resumed his position on the faculty of L'Ecole Central and had a very successful engineering career. After a few years of teaching he was appointed headmaster of L'Ecole Central. He continued his work in engineering and was well known and respected in engineering circles in France and other parts of Europe. French engineering journals of the time are filled with his articles. He also developed an interest in Egyptology and made significant contributions in the deciphering of hieroglyphics.

American science and technology, sorely in need of talent in the era of expanding industry, had lost a brilliant mind in the person of Norbert Rillieux. After the Civil War the sugar industry, with the increased production made possible by Rillieux's evaporator, was one of the prime movers in the economic recovery of the New Orleans region.

Rillieux continued an active and productive life until his death in 1894. A brief obituary appeared in a New Orleans newspaper in which references to his color and background were studiously avoided.

The multiple effect evaporator pioneered by Rillieux is now basic in the chemical industry. A statement on its importance was made by Charles A. Browne, a sugar chemist in the United States Department of Agriculture, who said, "I have held that Rillieux's invention is the greatest in the history of American chemical engineering, and I know of no other invention that has brought so great a saving to all branches of chemical engineering." Rillieux's evaporator was as significant a contribution to the American economy as McCormick's reaper, Whitney's cotton gin, Fulton's steamboat, and many other inventions commonly mentioned in history textbooks.

Rillieux's ideas have been summed up in various books as two or three basic principles that are axiomatic to all students of sugar refining and general chemical engineering. Many of Rillieux's papers have been lost, and it is not known when these principles were formulated or even if Rillieux himself so summarized his work. In a widely used book on sugar technology of South African publication, Rillieux's principles are fully discussed, but Rillieux is not mentioned by name.

The multiple evaporation principle is today widely used in other applications, such as the production of soap, milk, gelatin, glue, and in waste recovery processes in distilleries and paper mills.

After his return to France, Norbert Rillieux was almost completely forgotten in Louisiana and the rest of the United States. The sugar industry and Louisiana continued to profit from his invention, but there was little if any mention of him in histories of Louisiana and in sugar industry publications in the years following his death.

In 1934, after much evasion and delay, a plaque honoring Rillieux's contribution to Louisiana's sugar industry was erected in the Louisiana State Museum in New Orleans. In recent years there has been renewed interest in Rillieux's importance, and articles about him have appeared in many sugar industry journals.

Wires, Rails, and Shoes

The end of the Civil War and Reconstruction marks a great divide in American history. The all-consuming conflict over slavery and secession had been settled on the battlefield, and the energies of the people were turned from the destruction of war to more practical matters. More important than the change in the political scene was a very basic change in the American way of life. For scores of years before the Civil War, the United States had been mostly an agricultural nation. In the mere thirty-five years between the end of the war and the beginning of the next century, the United States was transformed from an inward-looking, pastoral country into the world's strongest industrial power.

There were many factors that contributed to this rapid economic growth and transformation. The large size of the United States assured an abundance of many natural resources such as iron and coal. There was also an abundance of capital, much of which came from foreign investors who saw great potential for profits in the sprawling, young country. The official policy of the American government was to encourage business growth, either by leaving it alone or enacting favorable legislation. An example of the latter was the granting of huge tracts of Federal lands to railroads, and the nation was soon linked by steel rails.

Perhaps the most important resource was the American people who were known all over the world as inventive, industrious, and ambitious. There was an ample labor force, swelled by tens of thousands of immigrants, who were attracted by the expanding economy. The first transcontinental railroad was built by Irish workers laying tracks from the East and by Chinese working from the West.

It was a great time for inventors. The demand for improved technology encouraged thousands of inventions related to transportation—especially railroads, communications, and improved techniques of industrial production. Some of the more significant inventions were the telephone, new methods of producing steel, and various devices utilizing electricity to provide light and power. Inventors, of course, hoped to make fortunes from the products of their minds, but, then as now, to make a fortune required much more than mechanical ingenuity. Some inventors, such as Thomas Edison and Alexander Graham Bell, did build empires based on their inventions. However, most inventors of this period died broke or near broke. Many an inventor found that financial know-how was more important than inventive know-how. It was men such as Andrew Carnegie and J. P. Morgan, who never invented a thing but who knew how to promote, distribute, and sell the inventions of others, who made fortunes so great as to make those of Edison and Bell look like piggy-bank collections. However, men with technological skills were in demand. They could make a fairly good living, and many did.

Inventors and other strivers were pushed by the belief that in the United States anyone with drive, ambition, and a little luck could make a fortune. And this belief was not entirely a myth. America was very much a mobile society in which a man did not necessarily have to remain in the social and economic level of his birth. The competition, however, was rough and the rewards were not forthcoming to the meek and polite. "Fair play" was not in the vocabulary of that rough, tough, unscrupulous breed of man who forged the American industrial fortress.

J. P. Morgan, Andrew Carnegie, John D. Rockefeller, and others like them were products of the American mobile society. In Europe of the time, with few exceptions, a man could not hope to advance his social status merely by the acquisition of money. Status was something one was born with, the sum total of hundreds of years of privileged ancestors who had been rewarded by long-dead kings for military and other services. Of course, inherited position made it somewhat easier to get into the situations that made making money possible. But the end was the position itself and not the money, which only helped one to maintain the position. In America, there were no inherited positions of nobility, and money was an end in itself. According to the American Dream, anyone could, by hard work, make a fortune, and by virtue of the fortune assume status in the eyes of his contemporaries. And whatever status was gained with money was lost as quickly as the money was lost.

The successful American industrialists and financiers were called "Captains of Industry" or "Robber Barons," among other things, depending upon one's point of view and economic position of the moment. The Rockefellers, Goulds, and Morgans ruthlessly shoved aside anyone who stood in the way of their empire building. In the process they forged such American corporate giants as United States Steel and Standard Oil. Many maintained that their tactics were justified because they benefited the general population by providing gainful employment for the masses and by providing the populace with an abundance of cheap goods and services.

According to economic theory, the empire-building activities of the Captains of Industry should indeed have spread various degrees of affluence and prosperity to the general populace. And the free economic atmosphere supposedly promised that anyone who wanted to could strive to be a Rockefeller and possibly make it. But far removed from the booming factories, the mansions at Newport, and the dinners at Delmonico's were thousands of Americans for whom the American Dream was a nightmare. There were vast numbers of people whose lives were a depression from cradle to grave. These were people who were effectively barred from competing for the dream and whose burdened backs made the dream more of a reality for others.

The conquered American Indians had been herded onto barren reservations where they were mostly forgotten except by agents of the Bureau of Indian Affairs—some of whom lined their pockets with funds intended for the welfare of the Indians. Immigrants sweated away their lives working in mines and factories for wages that hardly provided subsistence. Children as young as eight worked in factories and were sent down into the coal pits. The collective misery of the miners and factory workers spawned the great labor organizations.

Vying with the Indians for the dubious distinction of most forgotten American were the recently freed blacks. The Civil War had ended on a great note of hope for the *freedman. Slavery was gone and the conquering Federals and Reconstructionists had promised everything from forty acres and a mule to restored plantation mansions and boxes at the opera in exchange for votes to keep the Republicans in power. Even this sham was ended in 1876 when the Negroes were cast aside in a move of political expediency. The occasion for the betrayal of the American blacks was the "stolen election" of 1876. In return for the Democrats not making a fuss over the Presidential election being handed over to the Republican Hayes (even though the Democrat Tilden had clearly won), political power was returned to the southern whites and the blacks were left at the none too tender mercies of their former masters. The Republicans didn't need the blacks anymore. They had a new base of power in well-heeled northern industrialists. And before long the reestablished southern "Bourbons" saw to it that blacks would not be able to vote for anybody, the Fifteenth Amendment notwithstanding. The Republicans must have calculated well. Even though they lost the South they won ten out of the fourteen Presidential elections between 1876 and 1928.*

Repressive laws and Supreme Court decisions upholding these laws soon made Jim Crow segregation an overt way of life in the South and an only slightly less obvious reality in the rest of the country. Southerners justified the "new slavery" in much the same way that the old slavery had been justified. Negroes were declared to be inferior and fit only for menial work and to sing and dance for their own and the white man's amusement. In the South, patterns emerged which defined "white man's work" and "nigger's work." It was dangerous for a black man to aspire to "white man's work." Such aspirations might label him a "smart, uppity, nigger" and he could very well find himself dangling from the end of a rope. The black man found that he was the last hired in times of prosperity and first fired as soon as the economy slowed a bit.

Any time of industrial expansion, such as the post-Civil War era, presents opportunities for those with the right training and skills, technological or financial. American blacks were further kept out of entering the competition of the mobile society by lack of educational opportunity. Black children found it difficult if not impossible to go to school. And where schools for blacks existed, they were inferior to those for whites. Lack of earning power of black fathers forced many black children to forgo any attempt at education because of the necessity of working at an early age. The segregation laws had swept black Americans into a corner euphemistically called "separate but equal" but which really meant cut off from any attempt at attaining the American dream. That America was the loser because of the exclusion of blacks is evidenced by the absence of Norbert Rillieux. Rillieux, whose knowledge and skills could have been of further great value to American industry, had been hounded out of the country.

The environmental stagnation brought on by segregation reinforced the inferior status fiction propagated by the southern whites. "Look at how they live," was the frequently heard cry. Yet in spite of the burden of segregation and the superior attitudes of whites that held black men to be somewhat less than human, there were black men who did strive and attain a part of the dream in a country that did not even wish to acknowledge their presence as human beings. There were men, largely unnoticed, who made their mark in American science and invention.

So little notice was taken of black inventors that in 1909 a member of the Virginia State Legislature made a typical white southern speech in which he stated that no Negro had ever received a patent and this was, therefore, conclusive proof of the inferiority of the black man. This statement did not go unchallenged. A black man, named Henry Baker, employed as a clerk in the U. S. Patent Office, began to compile a list of inventions granted to blacks. He put his work together in a book entitled The Colored Inventor. *The book was nothing more than a listing of patents granted to acknowledged black men between 1863 and 1913. It listed some 1200 inventions. The number of black inventors was undoubtedly far greater. But many concealed their race in order to avoid one more obstacle. Although some of the inventions were as significant as the telephone and electric light, most of the black inventors received little recognition in their lifetimes. And most of them, as many other inventors, made little or no money from their inventions because they lacked the capital and connections to promote their work. It was very difficult for the black inventor to get financial backing, for the general attitude prevented many whites with money from investing in the inventions of black men. However, there are many instances of black inventors quietly selling their inventions to white men and white-controlled corporations.*

Black inventors made a large number of contributions to railroading with inventions related to lubrication of locomotives, coupling, communications, safety devices, and a variety of other devices ranging from berth registers to improved cow catchers. These inventions were made at a time when blacks were systematically excluded from the better jobs in railroading.

Railroads were the very heart and pulse beat of the industrial expansion of the post-Civil War era. Without them there could have been no industrial boom. Mass production and the distribution of goods to customers were completely dependent on the existence of an extensive network of railroads. Iron ore and coal moved on rails to the steel mills, and the steel from the mills was shipped to fabricators over the rails. Because of the railroads, any manufacturer could have the entire country as his customer.

It was evident that anyone who wanted to be a Captain of Industry would have to control or have considerable influence with one or more railroads. And some of the most vicious financial battles of the era were fought over the railroads. J. P. Morgan and Cornelius Vanderbilt made their fortunes from railroads even though neither of them ever dirtied his hands on a locomotive. John D. Rockefeller made his fortune in oil, but his control of railroads through acquisition, deals, and bribery was instrumental in the building of his oil empire. Railroad magnates vied with each other to give bigger bribes to Congressmen in exchange for favorable legislation.

It was one thing to acquire rights of way and lay rails and quite another to run them efficiently. The demand for railroad services frequently outran the ability of the lines to perform. Signaling equipment was crude and there were frequent accidents. Lack of equipment to bring trains to a safe stop limited the speed at which they could operate. Even coupling the cars was a slow and dangerous job. The smart young inventor saw inviting opportunities in the needs of the railroads, and many directed their entire attention to inventing better railroad equipment.

One of the most exasperating things about early railroading was the necessity of stopping at frequent intervals to oil the bearings and other friction points on locomotives. This was not something that could be overlooked or taken casually. Unlubricated bearings would heat up from the *friction and burn or seize. When this happened, it was "scatch one" locomotive while it was in the shop for repairs. Lubrication stops were expensive in time lost and in customer annoyance at late deliveries.*

Signals were primitive at best, and many a high-balling locomotive plowed into the rear of another train standing on the tracks as its locomotive was being oiled. The situation begged for solution, and the solution came from a man who was in a position to invent it, mainly because his parents had chosen to take a ride on a different kind of "railroad."

THE REAL MCCOY

The network of hiding places, secret routes, and various guises of the "Underground Railroad" was set up by abolitionists to help slaves escape to the northern states. Escape to the North was expedient until the Compromise of 1850, which called for a strict enforcement of the fugitive slave law. As a result of the compromise, no free black or escaped slave in the North was safe from gangs of slave catchers who roamed the northern states scooping up any dark-skinned human being they could find and catch. Many blacks then fled to Canada where it was cold but where they were safe from the long trip back to the hot plantations in Dixie Land.

Elijah McCoy's parents must have seen what was coming for they fled to Canada in 1840, and Elijah was born in Colchester, Ontario, on May 2, 1844.

After the war, the family moved back to the United States and settled near Ypsilanti, Michigan. Young Elijah had developed an interest in engineering but he could not obtain the necessary training in the States. So he went to Scotland where he learned mechanical engineering as an apprentice. Thus armed, he returned. Upon his return, he found that mechanical engineering was regarded as white man's work, and in spite of his training and skills, he could not find an engineering job. After many frustrating months of job hunting, he had to take a menial job as a fireman on the Michigan Central Railroad. With few exceptions, fireman was about as good a job a black man could expect to get on the expanding railroads. The fireman's job was to shovel the coal into the firebox and to oil the moving parts of the engine at the frequent intervals when the train had to stop for such oiling.

McCoy must have been impressed with the inefficiency of stopping the big engine in order to oil the bearings with a ridiculously small oil can. He was shrewd enough to see that here was something that cried out for invention and he started to work on it. He set up a crudely equipped machine shop in a shed and worked on the problem whenever he could find the time.

Locomotives were not the only machines that had to be shut down in order to be lubricated. Heavy machinery in factories also had to be so halted. McCoy concentrated his initial efforts on the lubrication problems of stationary factory machines, and in 1872 he was ready to apply for his first patent on a device he called a "lubricating cup." The problem and solution were succinctly stated in his description of the device in the patent application: ". . . provides for the continuous flow of oil on the gears and other moving parts of a machine in order to keep it lubricated properly and continuously and thereby do away with the necessity of shutting down the machine periodically."

McCoy's first lubricator, designed for use on stationary machinery, particularly steam engines, was essentially a system of tubes and valves that carried the lubricating liquid to various parts of the machine in measured and timed

Elijah McCoy. (*Courtesy of Lloyd Douglas*)

quantities. McCoy did not sit back and wait for the royalties to come rolling in. Even before the patent was granted, he had started to work on an improved version, if for no other reason than to keep ahead of the many imitators who always cropped up about a successful invention.

His improved model was ready only a year after his first patent was granted. The new version was designed to oil the parts when the steam was exhausted from the cylinders. This was the point in the machine's operation when lubrication was most needed. The lubricating cup was fitted directly into the cylinder. McCoy was granted Patent No. 139,407 for this device on May 27, 1873.

McCoy never stopped working on the problem that had originally commanded his attention—continuous lubrication

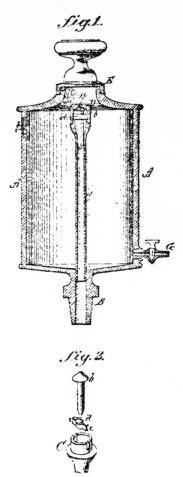

Fig. 1.

Fig. 2.

Witnesses
John A. Ellis
C. Absanier

Inventor
Elijah M. McCoy
Por.
J. N. Alexander & Co.
Attys

McCoy's lubricating cup, first version. (_Courtesy of United States Department of Commerce_)

for locomotives. The problems here were much more difficult than those involved in stationary machinery. Steam enters the cylinders at great pressures in locomotives, and in early locomotives this pressure precluded lubrication while the locomotive was in operation. The difficulty was in equalizing the pressure at critical points so that the lubricating oil could get into the cylinder. McCoy's solution to the problem was ingenious in its simplicity. And the less complicated a device is, the more reliable it is likely to be. He provided an auxiliary overflow pipe independent from the steam supply pipe, thereby achieving an equalization of pressure. Oil could then flow into the cylinder. No doubt many a would-be inventor said to himself, "Now why didn't I think of that?"

McCoy's invention was a small thing, but it speeded up the railroads, and faster railroad deliveries spurred the economic growth of a nation. McCoy's lubrication system was also applied to ship engines. His system quickly gained acceptance with many railroads and shipping lines, especially in the West and on the Great Lakes. As news of the efficiency of McCoy's lubrication system spread, most of the country's railroads had the devices fitted to their locomotives. Unfortunately, many of the lubricators that became available after McCoy obtained his patents were imitations and did not work as well as McCoy's system. Purchasers of machinery wanted to be sure that it had the McCoy lubrication system before they would buy. "Is it the real McCoy?" became the standard question before the prospective buyer would sign on the dotted line. And so a new expression became part of our language as the "Real McCoy" came to mean whatever was the best and genuine article as applied to all things.

McCoy continued to be active well into the twentieth century. In 1920 he secured patents extending his continuous lubrication idea to railroad brakes. Other inventors had obtained patents that applied McCoy's principles to almost all the moving parts of a locomotive as well as other machinery. In the course of a very active life, McCoy obtained patents on some fifteen inventions, including a new kind of ironing board and a lawn sprinkler.

McCoy himself never became very well known during his lifetime. Most of the men who insisted on the "Real McCoy" may indeed have been factory owners or railroad owners who discriminated against blacks in employment, and who never knew that the perfection they sought was the product of the genius of a black man.

THE BLACK EDISON

Young Granville T. Woods was lucky in those things considered to be good fortune for black children in America. He was born of free parents in Ohio in 1856, and that alone was a colossal piece of luck in a year when most American blacks were other people's property. His parents even managed to send him to school on a hit-or-miss basis, and that, too, was no small bit of luck for a black child in the land of the free. Even that sketchy education had to come to an end when he was ten. It was again the old pattern of the immediate need of a near-indigent family pushing aside the long-range benefits of education. That was the way it was for black boys, although at the time not too many white children continued schooling much beyond the age of twelve or thirteen. To have seen the inside of a classroom at all was quite an achievement for a black child in America in the 1860s.

Woods's luck stayed with him and he found a job in a railroad machine shop rather than pitching hay and manure in a stable, sweeping the halls of the local Elk's Lodge, or any number of unskilled, nowhere jobs that the righteous,

Granville T. Woods. (*Courtesy of Lloyd Douglas*)

good people of the land considered appropriate for the Sons of Ham. His job in the machine shop was menial enough —operating the bellows which kept the forge hot. Woods, however, was lucky enough to find a master machinist who was willing to teach him much of the trade. Woods's payment of most of his wages as "tuition" contributed much to the master machinist's willingness to tutor the aspiring young man.

At the age of sixteen, Woods left the machine shop to begin a period of wandering, which would take him over much of the United States and across the Atlantic Ocean several times. Just why Woods went on this sojourn is not clear. He may have thought he had obtained as much benefit from the machine shop as he could. Perhaps his natural curiosity drove him to see as much of the world as he could before he settled down.

He traveled first to Missouri where he got a job on a small railroad called the Iron Mountain Line. One look at his face dictated to Woods's employer that the young man before him would never be more than a fireman. But his luck continued. Woods was made a fireman almost immediately and his promotion to engineer followed in a year. At seventeen, he was one of the youngest railroad engineers of any color in the country.

At some point during his travels Woods made his own personal discovery of electricity, and in this form of energy he saw more promise than in either machine shops or working on the railroad. Electricity had just recently been utilized as a source of energy and power when Woods was a young man.

Only some fifty years earlier, in 1820, Hans Oersted had accidentally discovered that an electric current would cause a compass needle to deflect and had demonstrated the until then only suspected relationship between electricity and magnetism. Some ten years later, Michael Faraday produced a weak electric current by rotating a copper disk between the poles of a magnet, establishing the principle of electromagnetic induction. Joseph Henry, in America, had established the same principle a year before—that a current of electricity could be produced by a constantly changing magnetic field. The next step, motion from an electric current, followed, and in 1831 Henry made an electric motor that was essentially the reverse of the electric generator. The widespread use of the electric motor did not come until a half century later when certain improvements in the design of motors and power supplies were made. And many of these improvements came from the mind of Granville Woods.

By 1879 Edison had developed his carbon-filament electric light, and in 1882 he established the first central electric power station, which fed electricity to customers from an electromagnetic generator. A new civilization of ease and convenience was to be brought by electricity. Woods certainly did not guess wrong in determining that electricity was the force of the future.

Woods read whatever books on electricity he could buy or borrow. On occasion white friends would take out books from libraries, a favor necessitated by the fact that many libraries in Missouri and other parts of the South would not admit blacks to their hallowed halls.

Woods left the railroad in 1874 and went to work in a steel-rolling mill in Illinois. He may have been a victim of the "first fired" principle as applied to blacks following the financial panic of 1873 that resulted in an economic depression and consequent bad times for the railroads and other industries. The steel mill claimed only two years of his life and in 1876 he went East to take some courses in electrical technology. It is not known just where he obtained this training, although it was probably in New York.

In 1878 his newly acquired knowledge helped him to get a job as an engineer on a British steamer called the *Ironsides*. Two years at sea was quite enough for Woods, and in 1880 he was again in a locomotive as an engineer on the Danville and Southern Railroad. The two-year pattern was broken on the Danville and Southern. Less than a year later Woods was back in Ohio, in Cincinnati, where he eventually established his own company for developing, manufacturing, and marketing electrical apparatus.

Woods's active mind worked in many directions, and his first invention was not electrical but one that was apparently based on his observations of steam engines during his years of working for railroads and steamship lines. The patent for this invention was for an improved steam boiler furnace. This patent was followed by a veritable stream of inventions almost all of which were electrical in nature.

The same year he patented the steam boiler he obtained a patent on an improved type of telephone transmitter. Alexander Graham Bell had introduced his telephone some ten years earlier and was well established when Woods developed his instrument. Woods did not have the capital and backing to try to compete with Bell in setting up a telephone system. It was generally assumed that a welter of competing telephone systems would be confusing and rather ineffective in providing nationwide communication. Therefore, competitors to the Bell system were discouraged, and Woods was no exception.

Alexander Bell was apparently quite impressed with Woods's ability, so much so that he bought one of Woods's inventions. The device that attracted Bell's interest was an apparatus that combined features of the telephone and

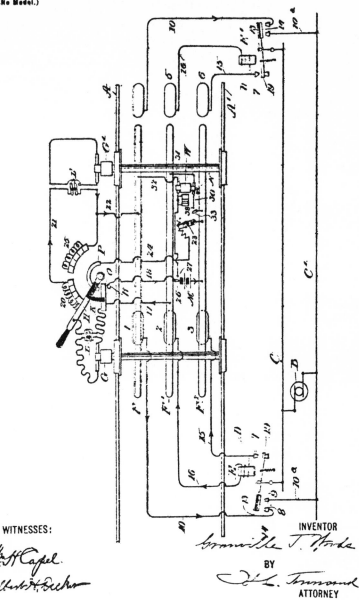

The "third rail." (*Courtesy of United States Department of Commerce*)

telegraph. Woods coined the word "telegraphony" for his system. The device enabled inexperienced operators to send and receive messages at a rate almost as fast as an experienced operator could with older equipment. It could be used for voice or Morse code transmission as the situation demanded. Woods obtained Patent No. 315,368 for this device in 1885, and the Bell Company purchased it shortly afterwards for an undisclosed large sum of money. It must have been sizable, for Woods was able to continue his inventing activities for the rest of his life and never again had to work on the railroad or in a steel mill.

Woods was apparently better known in his lifetime than contemporary histories indicate. His dealings with Bell and a series of inventions dealing with electric street railways attracted some notice. During the 1880s, horse-drawn street cars were rapidly replaced by vehicles powered by electric motors. The advent of the electric street car was due in no small measure to the work of Woods. The January 14, 1886, edition of the *American Catholic Tribune*, a nationally distributed newspaper, contained the following:

> Granville T. Woods, the greatest colored inventor of the race and equal, if not superior, to any inventor in the country is destined to revolutionize the mode of street car transit. The results of his experiments are no longer a question of doubt. He had excelled in every possible way in his inventions. He is master of the situation and his name will be handed down to coming generations as one of the greatest inventors of his time. He has not only elevated himself to the highest position among inventors but he has shown beyond doubt the possibility of a colored man inventing as well as one of any other race.

The inventions referred to in the article included a new

type of motor system and a device for collecting electric power from overhead wires.

One of the major problems involved in changing from horse-drawn street cars to electrically powered ones was the mechanism for controlling the speed by increasing and decreasing the current entering the armature. Electricity was, and still is, supplied to electric street cars from a central power station. It was, of course, not feasible to vary the current at the central power house. The amount of current entering the motors had to be regulated by devices right on the vehicle. This was accomplished by installing heavy resistance devices in the circuits. These resistance devices tended to become rather hot, and when they heated up they were very wasteful of electricity. At times they became so hot they caught fire, much to the horrified surprise of the passengers riding in the wooden street cars.

The system developed by Woods involved the introduction of secondary generators, called dynamotors, in the circuits, thus removing much of the load from the resistance devices. A dynamotor is a device that combines a generator and a motor in a single unit. The result was a cooler, more efficient operation, which not only saved money for the street car company owners, but provided a smoother and safer ride for the passengers as well.

Early electric street cars collected electricity either from a continuous wire running in a slot in the street or from overhead wires. There were problems involved with both methods. The narrow wheels of horse-drawn wagons frequently got caught in the slot. Many a wagon driver was quite startled on the occasions when he would turn his horse only to find that the wagon kept going straight because the wheels on one side of it were riding neatly in the street car slot. Power was picked up from the wire in the slot by a sliding "shoe." The sliding resulted in rapid wear of the pick-up shoe and the wire.

Overhead wires presented similar friction problems. Power was picked up with a sliding contact. The slider tended to jump the wire, especially at track switches. And, of course, the sliding wore down the contact and wires, which had to be replaced frequently.

Woods devised a grooved metal wheel which revolved at the end of a pole that extended from the top of the car to the overhead wire. The grooved wheel fitted onto the wire and revolved, effecting continuous contact as the car moved along. There was much less possibility of the grooved wheel jumping off the wire than had been the case with the sliding contact. The grooved wheel was called a "troller" or "trolley" and from its use came the name "trolley car."

In recent years, most American cities have discontinued the use of trolley cars in favor of buses. The exhaust fumes of buses have contributed to the air pollution problems of our cities, and many people now wish the trolley cars were still with us.

Woods made what was perhaps his most important invention in 1887. The invention was variously called the "multiplex telegraph," the "induction telegraph," and the "block system." Its major application was in railroading where it dramatically improved safety. That the invention was important was evidenced by the fact that Woods had to go through three patent suits to protect his rights. Two of these suits were instituted by Thomas Edison and the third by a man named Phelps. Woods was the winner in all three of the legal actions.

His induction telegraph was described in the *American Catholic Tribune* of April 1, 1887, which again found cause to praise Woods. Whoever wrote the article was so enthused that he elevated Woods to "the greatest electrician in the world."

Mr. Woods who is the greatest electrician in the world still continues to add to his long list of electrical inventions. The latest device he invented is the synchronous multiplex railway telegraph. By means of this system, the railway despatcher (*sic*) can note the position of any train on the route at a glance. The system also provides for telegraphing to and from the train while in motion. The same lines may also be used for local messages without interference with the regular train signals. The system may also be used for other purposes. In fact, 200 operators may use a single wire at the same time. Although the messages may be passing in opposite directions, they will not conflict with each other. In using the device there is no possibility of collisions between trains as each train can always be informed of the position of the other while in motion. Mr. Woods has all the patent office drawings for these devices as your correspondent witnessed.

The patent office has twice declared Mr. Woods prior inventor. The Edison and Phelps Companies are now negotiating a consolidation with the Woods Railway Telegraph Company.

The last paragraph alluded to an "if you can't beat them, join them" effort on Edison's part. After Woods won the court battles, Edison offered him a job and proposed to buy Woods's company. When Woods refused both of these offers, Edison offered to make Woods a partner in one of Edison's various enterprises, but Woods, preferring to be independent, also refused this attractive offer. At the time, Edison was involved in complicated financial matters related to establishing the first central electric power plant in New York. Edison had to establish his own companies for manufacturing various components of his electricity distribution system, and he was experiencing difficulty in obtaining the necessary capital. Woods's company and know-how would have been a welcome addition.

Edison had indeed invented a multiplex telegraph and obtained the first of a series of patents concerned with telegraph and stock tickers. But he was young and inexperienced at the time, and he did not take the trouble to protect his patents. Others reaped the benefits. Patent suits are complicated, drawn-out affairs, and the various parties in the suits are necessarily concerned with very fine points of technical detail. Woods's multiplex telegraph was similar to Edison's in many ways, but there were many important differences. Woods's applications of the multiplex principle to railroad communications and safety were original with Woods, and in the opinion of the court, Woods's features constituted sufficient originality to declare Woods the holder of the patents in question as they related to railroad communication.

By 1886, when Edison tangled with Woods, Edison had gone through hundreds of patent suits and was thoroughly disgusted with them. Edison, by this time, had left such matters to his lawyers and had become involved in a series of legal and financial battles, which would eventually result in his being "frozen out" of the electrical empire he had built.

After his legal victory over Edison, Woods was widely referred to as the "Black Edison." The Cincinnati *Sun* reported:

> Gr. T. Woods a young colored man of this city has invented a new system of electrical motor for street railroads. He has also invented a number of other electrical appliances and the syndicate controlling his inventions think they have found Edison's successor.

G. T. WOODS.

RAILWAY TELEGRAPHY.

No. 373,383.

Patented Nov. 15, 1887.

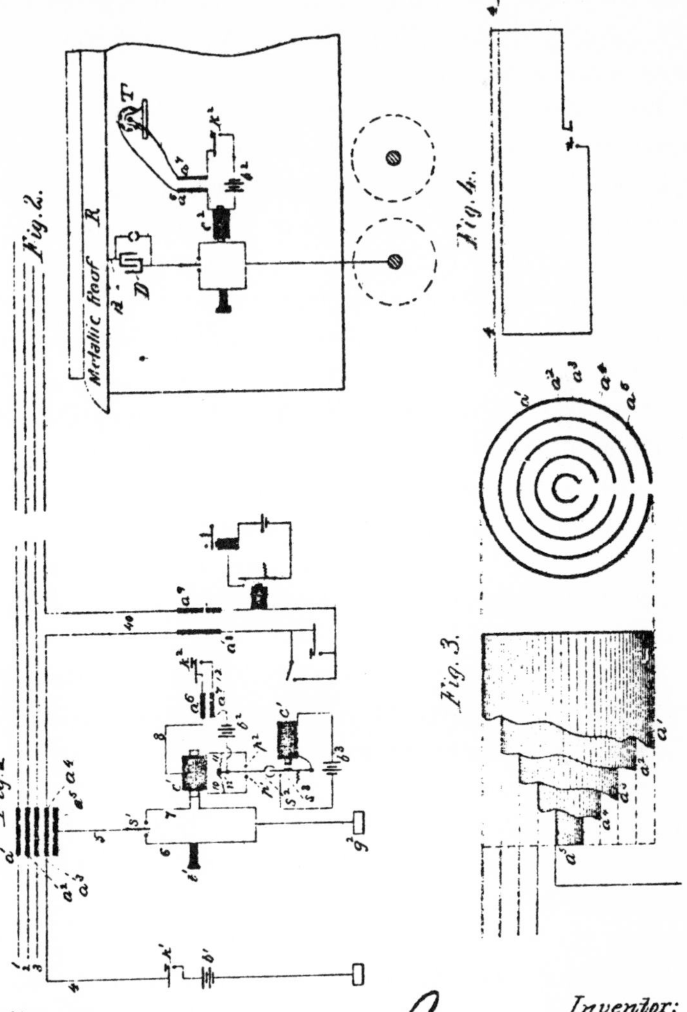

Fig. 2.

Fig. 4.

Fig. 3.

Fig. 1.

Witnesses:
W. C. Jirdinston.
S. L. Ker.

Inventor:
Granville T. Woods
by Roll Hosea
his Attorney.

Woods's multiplex telegraph. (*Courtesy of United States Department of Commerce*)

There were many parallels between Woods and Edison. Both had made significant achievements in spite of many obstacles, such as limited education and childhoods that could be described as "deprived." There is no doubt that Edison's inventions were very important and that they changed the American life style much more significantly than did those of Woods and most other inventors. Both men, however, lived long enough to see an age of technology that had no room for men such as themselves.

As the century drew to a close it was evident that the time was past when men such as Edison and Woods, who lacked advanced degrees and knowledge of theory, could make their way solely with their sweat and imagination, their guts and determination. The increased emphasis on formal education made even more obstacles for the black man who wanted to compete in the world of science and technology. It was almost impossible for most black men to obtain even the basic education necessary to be considered for admission to colleges and universities which set severe limitations on the numbers of black students they would admit into their hallowed halls. The Negro colleges, which had been started by Booker T. Washington and others, emphasized agricultural and artisan skills in their programs at a time when the artisan was already a thing of the past.

Woods saw what was coming and made statements to the effect that the young man who wanted to get ahead would have to get himself well educated and that men such as himself would soon no longer be able to function in the technological age. Edison was awakened perhaps somewhat rudely when he visited the General Electric plant in Schenectady in 1922. The General Electric Company had been formed from the consolidation of some of Edison's companies. There he witnessed the work of such geniuses as Langmuir and the amazing hunchback, Steinmetz. The employees at the plant gave Edison a cheering ovation as he entered the plant, but he sadly remarked as he left that the work of Langmuir and Steinmetz was completely beyond his understanding. Edison's close friend, Henry Ford, was perhaps the last of the old breed, and his tenacious clinging to the old ways and his mistrust of college-educated people destroyed his college-educated son, Edsel, and almost destroyed the Ford Motor Company.

Woods's inventions were in great demand, and he could have made a fair amount of money by devoting the rest of his life to manufacturing and marketing what he had invented by 1890. After he obtained the multiplex patents Woods reorganized his company as a manufacturing concern and called it Woods Electric Co. Woods, however, was not content to be an industrialist. He was an inventor and would let nothing keep him from inventing. In 1890 he shifted his base of operations to New York, probably because New York had more electricity than any other city. He was joined in his efforts from time to time by his brother, Lyates, who had several inventions to his own credit. Woods's Cincinnati company continued in existence for some years after his departure.

One of his first inventions after he went to New York was a system for dimming lights. His system utilized an auxiliary generator in the circuit, between the main generator and the switch, that varied the current, thereby effecting the dimming. It was essentially the same pinciple he had previously applied to trolley car motors. Before this resistors prone to overheating, and which were fire hazards, had been used. Such devices were extremely dangerous, especially in theaters where they were widely used, and they did indeed cause fires. Woods, quite a theater lover himself, had brought new safety and efficiency to show business.

It did not take long for Woods to make his presence known

in the big city. *Cosmopolitan* magazine, one of the most widely read periodicals of the time, published an article on him in the April 1895 issue, which included:

> Mr. Woods has taken out some thirty-five patents in various countries and has many still pending. He is the inventor of a telephone which he sold to the Bell Telephone Company, and of a system of telegraphing from moving railway trains which was successfully tried in the New Rochelle branch of the New Haven Road in 1885. Three years ago, an electric railway system of his invention was operated at Coney Island. It has neither exposed wires, secondary batteries, nor a slotted way. The current was taken from iron blocks placed at intervals of twelve feet between the rails, in which by an ingenious arrangement of magnets and switches, the current was turned on to the blocks only as they were successively covered by the cars . . .

The article went on to report that Woods had successfully defended his patents on the street car motor systems in no less than five patent suits.

The power pick-up system he developed for the Coney Island electric train was a precursor of one of his inventions that is part of the lives of millions of subway riders in New York and other big cities. This was the system of power collection known as the "third rail." The third rail is a conductor of electricity set parallel to the tracks. Each car is equipped with pick up "shoes" that ride along the conducting rail. With Woods's system each car became a power unit. Woods obtained Patent No. 667,110 on this system on January 29, 1901.

Woods's inventions speeded up the conversion of city transit systems from steam to electric power. Indeed, the work of Woods helped to make subways possible. Steam trains could operate well enough on the elevated structures that are still part of the scene in many large cities. But steam locomotives, belching clouds of black smoke, could not be used in subways. Subways are, of course, much preferred over the rather ugly elevated structures. Woods's inventions hastened the dismantling of many elevated structures and brought sunlight and renewed vigor back to many city thoroughfares.

From 1902 to 1905 Woods obtained patents on a system of improved air brakes. This air-brake system proved to be of interest to George Westinghouse, who had done some work on air brakes in the 1880s and had formed a company for selling them. Woods sold these inventions to Westinghouse.

Woods's inventions were now part of the everyday lives of millions of people. They rode street cars and subways powered by Woods's motors, supplied with electricity by Woods's electricity transfer devices, and brought to safe stops by Woods's improved air brakes.

Even the Sunday chicken dinner was influenced by Woods's inventiveness, for in 1890 he had invented a thermostatically controlled egg incubator. Woods's roster of inventions include an electromagnetic brake for electric motors, a safety cutout for electric currents (circuit breaker), and even an electrical amusement device. When he died in 1910 he had some sixty patents to his credit. Many of his patents were assigned to the General Electric Company, the American Engineering Company, Westinghouse Air Brake Company, and the Bell Telephone Company.

Electricity has made everyone's life easier, and many of the applications of electricity, which are accepted without question as necessary adjuncts of our lives, were made possible by the genius of Granville T. Woods.

THE IMPOSSIBLE MACHINE

Most of the tourists who go on cruises to the Caribbean Islands and South America are enraptured with the tropical beauty of these places. "How lovely. I wish I could live here all the time," are the frequent comments of the tourists. They have but to leave the shore-front markets, bazaars, and night clubs and travel a short distance to the unbelievable squalor of the slums of these places to see that not all is the music-filled, blossom-scented romance of tropical nights.

The prevalent pattern in the British, French, and Dutch colonies was that as the black slaves were freed they occupied the lowest rung on the social and economic ladder. Political and economic power was held by the few whites —colonial administrators, merchants, and businessmen. The black majority was kept in the shanties to scramble for whatever economic crumbs might fall their way. Many blacks left the Caribbean countries to come to the United States at a time when the situation for blacks in America was particularly bleak. As bad as things were in the United States, there was at least the mobile society with its faint hope that through hard work one could make somewhat of a place for himself. For a black in Surinam, Tobago, Anguilla, or any of these tropical paradises the mobile society did not exist.

Jan Matzeliger, born in Paramaribo, Surinam (Dutch Guiana), on September 12, 1852, was more fortunate than most. His father was in charge of the government machine works. And at the age of ten, Jan was sent to work as an apprentice in these same works. At nineteen, in 1871, he signed up as a seaman on a merchant steamer. He must have known that he would never return to Surinam for he carried with him some green nutmegs and coffee beans preserved in a jar of alcohol. He kept this memento of Surinam for the rest of his life.

In 1873 or 1874 he left the ship at Philadelphia and spent two or three years there at various odd jobs. In 1876 he was in Boston, and in that same year he settled in Lynn, Massachusetts, a town on the North Shore of Boston Harbor.

At the time, Lynn was one of the leading shoe-manufacturing centers in a state that produced well over half the nation's shoes. Matzeliger went to Lynn with absolutely no prospects other than the vague hope of finding a job in a shoe factory. Just why he chose Lynn and the shoe industry is not clear. He probably had some cobbling experience in Philadelphia and may have become intrigued with the mechanics of shoe manufacturing as a result of this experience.

His reception in Lynn was not exactly enthusiastic. No welcome wagon greeted the young Dutch-speaking immigrant. Lynnites were not accustomed to black people among them, and responses to his job-hunting efforts ranged from polite no's to demands that he remove his dark-skinned self immediately from the premises. His persistence was eventually rewarded, and he found a job as an operator of a McKay sole sewing machine. He had apparently obtained some experience on this machine, or on one like it, in Philadelphia. This was only the first of many jobs in the shoe factories of Lynn.

He was a deeply religious man, although when he came to Lynn he had never been a member of any particular church. He always wore a rectangular lapel button which bore the legend, "Safe With Jesus."

Matzeliger eventually became quite popular with the young set in Lynn. He was friendly with the other young workers in the factories, and he knew practically every young person in town through a part-time job he had driving a horse-drawn coach to and from Raddin's Grove, a picnic park in West Lynn. He attended night school and learned English so well that he spoke with not a trace of an accent. Matzeliger tried to attend the Catholic, Episcopal, and Unitarian churches in Lynn. The pious members of these churches chose not to have a dark-skinned man join them in their worship. This series of rejections embittered Matzeliger, not against religion but against the particular churches that had refused him, and he nurtured the grudge.

The Christian Endeavor Society was the very active and ebullient youth group of the North Congregational Church. Matzeliger knew all of the bouncy young people in this group and he was very popular with them. In 1884 they invited him to become a member. He never was a full member of the church, but he attended services, taught Sunday school, and helped actively with the picnics, bazaars, and other church functions. He even took part in amateur theater productions.

Matzeliger had not come to Lynn just to work in one shoe factory after another. He was an opportunist and determined

J. E. MATZELIGER.
LASTING MACHINE.

No. 274,207.

Patented Mar. 20, 1883.

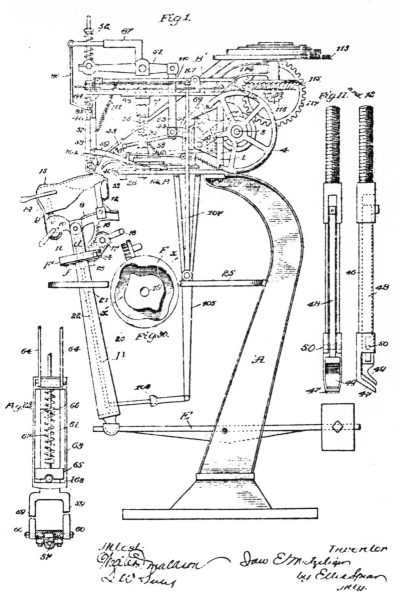

Matzeliger's first lasting machine. (*Courtesy of United States Department of Commerce*)

to put his machine skills to profitable use. He tried working on a railroad car coupler, an orange wrapping machine, and an automatic shoe sewer before he turned to the problem that was so obvious, a shoe-lasting machine.

By the 1880s the shoe industry had become one of the more mechanized in the nation. Operations such as sewing, eyelet insertion, and buffing were carried out by machine. There was one vital operation, however, that had not yielded to mechanization efforts. And that was lasting. Lasting is the process of attaching the upper leather portion of the shoe to the inner sole. When Matzeliger started to work on the problem lasting was done by hand in much the same manner it had been done since Colonial times.

Lasting was a complicated procedure that required highly skilled craftsmen. Matzeliger prepared himself for his big task by closely watching the hand movements of the lasters and by studying physics and practical mechanics both from books and by experimentation. Matzeliger spent as much time as he could watching the hand lasters. In the process of lasting, the craftsman would first lock the last in a holding jack or vise. The last is a wooden model of the human foot. Leather is not a uniform substance. It comes from the cow in infinite varieties of thickness and degrees of hardness and softness. Soft leathers had to be pulled over the last tightly, almost to the point of tearing. If the leather was not tight enough over the last, the leather would wrinkle in the course of usage. When the operator judged that the leather had been drawn over the last properly, the edges of the upper leather were tacked to the innersole. The excess leather at the toe was cut and drawn into plaits which were shaved off to produce a smooth surface when it was attached to the outer sole, usually by sewing. Matzeliger had set himself the task of building a machine that would duplicate all of these complex operations as carried out by a skilled artisan.

Matzeliger was not the first to attempt making a shoe-lasting machine. The demands of the shoe industry had stimulated many earlier attempts. Since everything but lasting had been mechanized, hand lasting had turned out to be a serious bottleneck. Hand lasters could not keep pace with the machines. Machines stood idle from time to time as they ran ahead of the hand lasters. The situation was proving to be quite costly for the industry. Many earlier attempts, especially in England, had been unsuccessful. Some, such as the machine put together by the Americans, Pennington and Weeks, had even been patented and marketed, but they just did not perform in actual use.

Gordon McKay, the inventor of the machine that had provided Matzeliger's first job in Lynn, had worked on a lasting machine in the 1870s. He had even organized a company for the sole purpose of developing such a machine. He bought up existing patents on unsuccessful machines and hired some of the best talent in the country, including the inventors of the machines whose patents he had bought. One unsuccessful machine, the Thompson, had cost its inventor a hundred thousand dollars in development costs. McKay and a man named Glidden spent four years and well over an additional $120,000 in their efforts. In today's money, this would be about a million dollars. This massive effort of money and mechanical talent failed to produce a working lasting machine. The experience convinced shoe manufacturers that a lasting machine was impossible. Matzeliger, however, was not so convinced. And with no assets other than his meager salary and his fertile brain he set

out to succeed where the combined talents of some of the
country's best mechanical engineers and hundreds of thousands of dollars had failed.

There are many stories of men who accidentally stumbled
onto great scientific discoveries and great inventions. Such
was not the case with Matzeliger. He very deliberately
set the development of a workable, practical lasting machine
as his goal. Encouragement for this difficult task came
only from himself. The frustrating experiences of those who
came before him offered only discouragement. Matzeliger
apparently did not clutter his mind with the details of
previous attempts. He intensified his "research" of closely
watching the hand movements of the hand lasters. The
hand lasters knew that a working machine might cost them
their jobs. But they, as everyone else in the shoe industry,
believed that a lasting machine was an impossibility, so they
felt amused rather than threatened by Matzeliger's efforts.

To save money, Matzeliger moved into a room on the
top floor of the West Lynn Mission, a squat frame structure
in a rather seedy section of the city. It lacked heating and
many other amenities, but it was cheap and Matzeliger
needed every spare penny. With used drafting tools he
drew plans, and in the fall of 1880 he had constructed a
model out of bits of cigar boxes, paper, pins, and assorted
hardware. He tried to keep his work secret, but word of
it got around and he was the butt of many jokes. Someone,
however, thought enough of his cigar-box model to offer him
fifty dollars for it.

Not everyone thought his efforts a joke. He developed
a lasting friendship with two girls, Enna Jordan and Bessie
Lee. The latter was a button-hole machine operator in
one of the factories in which Matzeliger had worked.
The two girls extended many kindnesses to him and offered

him encouragement at a time when most everyone else in town ridiculed him and treated him rather roughly. Enna, who worked at a refreshment stand in Raddin's Grove, frequently invited him home for supper, which must have been gratefully received by Matzeliger, for he had allowed himself only five cents a day for food and was subsisting on corn-meal mush. Both girls shared their lunches with him. In gratitude, Matzeliger took time from his consuming work to make a lunch pail for Enna and toys for Bessie's younger brother, Percie. Matzeliger, in addition to his other talents, was an accomplished amateur painter, and he gave Enna a painting for a wedding present. There is evidence that Matzeliger's feeling for Bessie Lee was somewhat stronger than that of just a good friend. But he had little money and what he had went for supplies needed to work on the lasting machine. He felt that he was in no position to support a wife. Bessie Lee eventually left Lynn and went to live in Maine.

The cigar-box model looked promising, but it certainly would not last any shoes in a factory. Matzeliger had to build an actual working model out of iron and steel, which required a number of things he did not have, such as a suitable place to install the machine, and money to buy tools and parts. The first problem was solved by the kindness of an employer. He got a job at the Beal shoe factory and the owner gave him some floor space. Matzeliger partitioned off this space so that he could work in privacy and relative secrecy. There were many who would have eagerly pirated his ideas. The second problem was not so easily solved. Matzeliger scoured the junk yards and the factory cast-off heaps for parts of discarded machines. Many of the parts he needed were not in existence, since he had designed them specifically for his machine. This meant machining parts to order, an expensive matter which Matzeliger could not afford. He adapted existing parts of machines for his own needs by filing them to fit and with the help of borrowed lathes and other tools. Matzeliger became quite discouraged at this point. Others, such as the McKay group, had failed although they had all the money they needed for machining parts, and here he was trying to make an unbelievably complicated machine with cannibalized bits of other broken machines!

Despite his efforts at secrecy it became known, much to everyone's amazement, that Matzeliger was making real progress toward the "impossible." Someone offered him fifteen hundred dollars for his machine and Matzeliger may have been sorely tempted to take it. Miraculously, Matzeliger managed to put together an iron model with odd parts, but he knew it would not hold up to a severe factory testing with the jerry-rigged parts. Certain parts had to be made to order and made with great precision. He had to find financial backing.

Matzeliger found his backers, but the price was high. Two local business men, C. H. Denlow and M. S. Nichols, agreed to provide him with the funds he needed in exchange for two-thirds ownership of the invention. Matzeliger had reached the impasse that so many inventors before and after him had to face—sell out or quit. And he found, as had many others, that the really big rewards often went to those who knew more about manipulating dollars than manipulating gears and levers.

With the help of Denlow's and Nichols' money, Matzeliger built his prototype and submitted drawings and specifications to the patent office. The people at the patent office could not understand the machine from the drawings, and furthermore, they did not believe that so fantastically

Fourth version of Matzeliger's lasting machine, patented after his death. (*Courtesy of USM Corporation*)

complicated a machine could work. Finally, a patent examiner traveled to Lynn to examine the machine and was apparently satisfied with it since Matzeliger received Patent No. 274,207 dated March 20, 1883.

Receiving a patent was by no means the end of the work or the end of the anxiety. Other lasting machines had been patented only to fail miserably under factory conditions. It was not until the spring of 1885 that factory tests could be arranged. The tests were enormously successful. The machine clicked and clanked steadily without a hint of a breakdown. It lasted shoes ten times as fast as a hand laster could, and it did so with quality equal to that of a hand laster. Matzeliger, however, noted certain things that needed improvement, and over the next two years he obtained more patents on these specific improvements. The machine pulled the leather over the last at the proper degree of tension, placed the innersole in position, fed nails, drove the nails, cut, plaited and smoothed the toe! Shoe men had to see it to believe it. The impossible had been accomplished.

Denlow and Nichols were, of course, anxious to go into production and marketing. But they found themselves in somewhat the same situation as Matzeliger had several years before. It was one thing to provide a destitute inventor with a few hundred dollars to get some parts made at the local machine shop, and quite another to set up a producing factory and a system of distribution. The two gentlemen just did not have enough money. They had to turn to people who did. There followed a series of deals, acquisitions, mergers, stock swaps, etc., as complicated as Matzeliger's machine itself. Denlow and Nichols were eventually swallowed up in the financial quicksand and Matzeliger was left holding the short end of a sheaf of stock certificates.

Denlow and Nichols invited a pair of financiers, George W. Brown and Sidney Winslow to invest in the lasting machine enterprise. Winslow had a reputation as a "wheeling and dealing" machinery magnate and had previously been involved with sewing machines and other shoe machinery. Out of this deal came the Consolidated Shoe Machinery Company. The company took over Matzeliger's patents and Matzeliger received a block of stock. The company started rapid production of the machine while Matzeliger occupied himself with developing improved versions.

The lasting machine rapidly gained acceptance over competing lasting machines. Adaptation to changes in shoe styles, which had been a problem with earlier machines, was no problem for Matzeliger's. Factories increased production from fifty or seventy-five pairs a day to as many as seven hundred pairs a day, depending on the quality of the work. Flexibility in the quality of the product was another advantage that Matzeliger's laster had over its competitors.

In all the frenzy, Matzeliger was almost forgotten. Users of his machine came to refer to it as the "Niggerhead Laster," a name that persisted for many years after his death. Although Matzeliger did not make a fraction of the money the financiers reaped from his work, he did realize some earnings. He was able to move out of the cheap room in the West Lynn Mission, but the years in that place had weakened his general health.

A church picnic that he attended in 1886 was rained out, and the cold he caught developed into tuberculosis, a disease so prevalent among shoe workers as to approach the status of an occupational hazard. He began to board with a man named Barber Durgin and his wife. Durgin was a hand laster and the fact that he and wife took care of Matzeliger indicated that the lasters had no malice

THUMB TACKS USED ON
JAN MATZELIGER'S DRAFT-
ING BOARD

Portrait of Matzeliger, lunch box he made for Enna Jordan,
drafting board tacks, and his Bible. (*Courtesy of A. E. Klein*)

against him. Many lasters found jobs as operators of Matzeliger's machine and their lives were easier and longer for it. Eventually, because of the increased production and lower prices made possible by Matzeliger's machine, there were more jobs for lasters and other shoe workers than ever before.

The Durgin house was not very large, so Matzeliger bought a bigger one, which he rented to the Durgins while he continued to live with them as a boarder. He was still working on improved versions of his machine, and by 1888 had received a patent on a third model. At the time, he also worked on an improved type of electric motor. Work on a fourth version of the lasting machine stopped when he became so ill that he was bedridden. Matzeliger had a steady stream of visitors, and the deacon of the North Congregational Church regularly brought communion to his bedside. Matzeliger continued to weaken, and despite intensive medical care, he died on August 24, 1889, three weeks short of his thirty-eighth birthday.

In his will, Jan Matzeliger was generous with those who had been kind to him and vindictive with those who had spurned him because of his color. He bequeathed stock to the North Congregational Church with the following stipulations:

> . . . to be used in such a manner as he deems fit and proper towards the support and comfort of those he deems Christian poor of . . . Lynn, irrespective of religious denomination or societies, except that it shall not knowingly be given or expended for any member of the Roman Catholic, Unitarian, and Episcopal churches . . .

The rest of his assets were left to Lynn Hospital physicians and to about fifteen of his friends, including the Durgins.

Matzeliger in costume for an amateur dramatic production; possibly Gilbert and Sullivan's *Mikado*. (*Courtesy of Lynn Historical Society*)

Jan Matzeliger's story does not end with his death. Work on the fourth version of the machine was continued by some of Matzeliger's associates, and a patent was received in 1891. Matzeliger received posthumous recognition in 1901 when his machine was awarded a gold medal at the Pan American Exposition in Philadelphia. Some of the most advanced machinery of the time was shown at this exhibition. Matzeliger's influence continued to be felt in many ways more profound than gold medals. Some fifteen years after his death, the North Congregational Church fell into a serious financial crisis. The church was unable to meet its mortgage payments and was in danger of foreclosure.

The church was saved by the block of stock left to it by Jan Matzeliger. The many mergers and consequent stock splits had resulted in about a tenfold increase in the original value of the stock. Sale of the stock raised almost eleven thousand dollars, which was more than enough to pay off the mortgage. A special service of thanks was held in memory of the benefactor who had never even been a full member of the church. At the service, a large portrait of Matzeliger was dedicated, and this portrait hung in the vestry of the old church building in Lynn. The North Congregational Church later merged with another church to form the First Church of Christ Congregationalist. The portrait, along with Matzeliger's Bible and the lunch pail he had made for Enna Jordan, can still be seen today, in the new church on Lynnfield Avenue in Lynn. His drafting instruments and some other items are in a museum in Lee, Maine, a town founded by Percie Lee, who as a boy had received gifts of toys made by Matzeliger.

The corporate structure that grew around Matzeliger's lasting machine continued to expand after his death. The profits Winslow accrued from the success of the Matzeliger machine enabled him to overtake the McKay organization, which had previously been the leader in the shoe machinery field. In 1897 Winslow's Consolidated Hand Method Lasting Machine Company merged with the McKay Lasting Association. The new combine, called the Consolidated and McKay Lasting Machine Company, then bought up several smaller shoe machinery companies. It was not long before the remaining shoe machinery companies fell before the momentum of Winslow's corporate giant. In 1899 the Goodyear Shoe Machinery Company, the last of McKay's companies (called the McKay Shoe Machinery Company), and most of the holdouts among the smaller companies were absorbed by Winslow's Consolidated and McKay. The various acquisitions were reorganized into the United Shoe Machinery Company, the largest shoe machinery company in the world, which held a virtual monopoly of shoe machinery well into the 1950s, when the patents expired. And it was Matzeliger's laster that had made this industrial behemoth possible.

Thousands of young men have been helped by the fortunes Matzeliger helped to build for others. Donald McKay became wealthy as a partner in the United Shoe Machinery Company, and he set up the McKay Institute for Negro Boys in Kingston, Rhode Island. He also left six million dollars in scholarship funds to Harvard—through investments, this fund has grown to fifteen million.

May 22 has been designated as Jan Matzeliger Day in Lynn, and in recent years various observances have been held on this day to honor the memory of this man, who in a tragically short life accomplished the "impossible."

AMBITION'S COURSE IS PAVED
WITH HOPES DEFERRED

The activities of the fiery abolitionist, William Lloyd Garrison, were frequently a source of irritation to the citizens of Boston. Bostonians had a low opinion of slavery, but they frequently had an even lower opinion of a man who called them "agents of Satan" and worse, just because they did not share the vehemence of his uncompromising stand against slavery. Garrison believed that slaveowners were criminals and should be treated as such. Various schemes of compensating slaveowners for freeing their slaves, that had been proposed by more moderate abolitionists, were vigorously denounced by Garrison who proclaimed that criminals should not be rewarded for their crimes. Many Americans were afraid that Garrison's fanaticism might lead to the destruction of the Union. And that would have been fine with Garrison if it meant he no longer had to live in a country that harbored evil slaveowners. Even Frederick Douglass, the eloquent ex-slave abolitionist crusader, felt that Garrison frequently did the abolitionist cause more harm than good.

On one occasion, Garrison was nearly lynched by a mob of angry Bostonians. He was saved, but many, who were equally as opposed to slavery as Garrison, would not

have wept too long had this very irritating man met his
end on the Boston Common. But even those who were
annoyed with Garrison rallied behind him in support of
an ex-slave named George Latimer who had escaped to
Boston in 1831. The cause for rallying was the appearance
of Latimer's ex-owner, who had turned up in Boston in
1842 to claim his property. The case of the slaveowner was
very clear. He had documents to prove that Latimer was
his slave, and according to the laws of the land, the unfortunate Latimer had to go back to Virginia with him.

The citizens of Boston were outraged and were determined that Latimer would not return to slavery. There
were speeches and rallies and the entire city was taken
up in the excitement and emotion of the issue. There was,
however, only one way to save Latimer, Garrison's anti-
compensation stand notwithstanding. And that was to buy
him from his owner. Four hundred dollars was raised by
the enthusiastic supporters of Latimer, and his freedom was
bought. The means of obtaining the ex-slave's freedom was
very distasteful to Garrison, who probably would have preferred to throw the slaveowner into Boston Harbor as though
he were so much tea.

The excitement was over, and the Bostonians who had
rallied to Latimer's cause went back to their everyday
business and promptly forgot him. Latimer settled in nearby
Chelsea, and he and his wife had four children, among them
a boy named Lewis, who was born in 1848. Now that
George Latimer was no longer the object of the collective
emotional fever of Boston, he found he experienced the
same rejections and the same near impossibility of making
a living for himself and his family that most black men
experienced. So in 1858 he deserted his wife and children.
He was only one of many who fled from the futility and

humiliation of having his role as the provider constantly undermined.

Lewis Latimer was ten years old when his father left, and the young Lewis was not a stranger to work. Even before the elder Latimer left, Lewis had had an after-school job hawking Garrison's newspaper, *The Liberator*. Afterwards, he had to leave school to find work that would bring in more money than selling newspapers. He worked at a variety of jobs until 1864, when he joined the Navy at the minimum age of sixteen. Latimer served for the remainder of the Civil War on a vessel called the U.S.S. *Massasoit*. His brothers served in the Army. Latimer was assigned the rank of "landsman," which is roughly equivalent to the present-day naval rank of seaman.

After his honorable discharge in 1865 he got a job as an office boy in the patent law firm of Crosby and Gould. Latimer got the job because he could draw fairly well, and one of his duties was to assist the draftsmen who made the detailed drawings for his employer's clients. Latimer wanted to be a full draftsman, so with a set of used drafting instruments, borrowed books, and the aid of some interested draftsman friends, he learned enough to bolster his courage and persuade his boss to let him do some drawings. His work was, apparently, of very high quality, for he was eventually made chief draftsman of the firm. Alexander Graham Bell retained the firm of Crosby and Gould to handle the patent application for his telephone in the mid-1870s. And it was Latimer who executed the drawings on the Bell telephone patent.

Latimer started to invent while he was employed at Crosby and Gould. His first invention was one not usually discussed in the Victorian parlors of the time, but one that made travel a good deal more comfortable: "Water

Closets for Railroad Cars." For this device he was granted Patent No. 147,363 on February 10, 1873.

In a short period of time Latimer had advanced to a position much higher than a black man of the post-Civil War period could have hoped to achieve in a lifetime. Yet, in 1880 Latimer left Crosby and Gould to go to work as a draftsman for Hiram Maxim's United States Electric Lighting Company, then located in Bridgeport, Connecticut. During his years with Crosby and Gould, Latimer had surmised that electricity was the thing of the future. His desire to be a part of the rapidly growing and exciting field of electricity must have been very strong, for he left a secure, well-paying position for the uncertainties of an association with the enigmatic genius Maxim, who, in his autobiography, used the word "nigger" in its most derogatory sense.

Hiram Maxim engaged in inventive enterprises ranging from electric lights to steam-powered airplanes, to machine guns and other weapons of war. He is perhaps best known for the rapid-fire machine gun that bears his name. The use of his gun, which had been turned down by the American military but was eagerly adopted by the Germans, littered the battlefields of World War I with tens of thousands of corpses.

Maxim makes no mention of Latimer in his autobiography, even though Latimer's inventions proved to be quite profitable for him. At the time, Maxim and Edison were in fierce competition. Maxim claimed to be the prior inventor of the incandescent lamp (as did many others) and the two men were locked in a long series of legal battles. Pending the outcome of the various litigations, Maxim and the other claimants were free to engage in the electric light business.

The early light bulbs had filaments made of carbon or various carbonized materials. One of Latimer's first jobs at U. S. Electric was to work on problems of improving the quality of the light and the longevity of the filament. In 1881 he and J. V. Nichols, another Maxim employee, secured a patent for "certain new and useful improvements in incandescent electric lamps." The improvements involved a better method of bonding carbon filaments to the fine metal wires at the base of the lamp. This invention is recorded as Patent No. 247,097, dated September 13, 1881.

His next patent, No. 252,386, dated January 17, 1882, was for "A Process of Manufacturing Carbons." The carbons made from Latimer's process lasted a good deal longer than any of the others around at the time. This particular process must have pleased Maxim greatly, for the filaments were cut from blanks that could be made into any shape desired, and Maxim began to produce his electric lamps with M-shaped filaments.

At the time, electric arc lamps were still in wide use and were manufactured by Maxim. An electric arc lamp is basically two rods of carbon supported in such a way that there is a small gap between them. When a current of electricity is sent through the carbons, the current jumps the gap and a very bright, intense, blue-white light is produced. In 1882 Latimer devised a "Globe Support" for arc lights, and for this he received Patent No. 255,212. Carbon arc lamps are still used in aerial search lights and in some film projectors. These lamps never achieved much success as home lighting. They made a very annoying hissing noise, and the carbons were very rapidly consumed.

For a while, in the 1880s, Maxim gave Edison a good fight in securing customers. Maxim landed some of the choicest contracts for installing electric lights such as the Equitable Building, at the time one of New York City's largest office buildings, and the Union League Club. Latimer was put in charge of these installations. Maxim also did well in European operations and was operating in England as the Maxim-Weston Company. In 1881 Latimer was in London supervising the production of carbon filaments at Maxim-Weston with the method he had invented. Although Latimer and his wife enjoyed London, the job was not altogether pleasant. The Victorian Britishers who ruled millions of black people in their world-wide empire were not used to taking orders from a black man. The job, however, was accomplished and Maxim's London operation was soon profitably producing light bulbs. Latimer also did installation jobs in Philadelphia and some Canadian cities.

After the London experience, Latimer left Maxim and worked for a couple of smaller electric companies before accepting a job with Edison in 1884. During this time Edison and Maxim continued to swap legal blows, and in 1886 Edison was quite startled when a judge in St. Louis ruled in favor of Maxim on the grounds of a technicality. Edison, of course, appealed, but in the meantime Maxim continued to have a free hand. The litigations dragged on for another three years, and in the meantime Latimer worked in Edison's engineering division at 65 Fifth Avenue in New York City. During these years a series of financial moves resulted in the formation of the Edison General Electric Company and Maxim's U. S. Electric was acquired by Westinghouse. Finally, in 1891, Edison's incandescent bulb patents were confirmed by the United States Circuit Court of Appeals of the Southern District of New York, and there is evidence that the expertise of Lewis Latimer played no small role in Edison's legal victory.

Since Latimer had worked for Maxim, Edison and his attorneys no doubt called on Latimer for advice. Latimer's

Lewis Latimer (front on right side of table) at the founding meeting of the Edison Pioneers. (*Courtesy of Edison National Historic Site; National Park Service*)

value was seen, and he was transferred to the legal department of Edison General Electric in 1890. Latimer helped to prepare the cases against Maxim and others as the Legal Department's chief draftsman and expert witness. Westinghouse-Maxim did not surrender easily, and they too, appealed. The final verdict in Edison's favor came in 1892. There was not much joy in the victory, however. Edison's patents only had two years to run anyway.

Westinghouse and Edison had been engaged in a different kind of fight in the 1880s, and this fight was called "the battle of the currents." Edison used direct current (DC) while Westinghouse supplied his customers with alternating current (AC). Alternating current could be sent over greater distances, but Edison claimed it was dangerous. Most of the electricians of the day knew that alternating current was superior and really the only way to supply large numbers of customers with electricity. Edison stubbornly held to his contention, and he even staged some rather grisly demonstrations in which various animals were electrocuted with alternating current. He even promoted the adoption of the electric chair (powered by AC), hoping that the use of AC for such an unpleasant purpose would convince people of its dangers. Even most of Edison's men, Latimer included, knew that AC was the current of the future and they looked for some way for Edison to back down gracefully.

After Westinghouse was beaten in the patent suits, a series of secret conversations between the Edison and Westinghouse groups was initiated with a merger as the goal. Such a merger had many advantages, including the opportunity to change to AC and still save face for Edison. The merger never did come off, and Edison continued to attack AC as unsafe. A series of other mergers and acquisitions, however, resulted in a reorganization, and the Edison General Electric Company became the General Electric Company. Before Edison knew what had happened he found both himself and direct current politely shoved aside.

Both Westinghouse and Edison General Electric had been nearly bankrupted by the many years of patent litigation, and they resolved to take steps to prevent such expensive occurrences in the future. To that end, the two companies, in 1890, formed a board of patent control, and Latimer was made the chief draftsman and expert witness of this board. Not only did the board effectively prevent further litigation between Westinghouse and Edison General Electric, it also protected the two companies against patent encroachment from others. The board was dissolved in 1911, when the two companies could no longer agree on certain aspects of its operation.

Latimer was a devoted family man and active in com-

J. V. NICHOLS & L. H. LATIMER.
ELECTRIC LAMP.

No. 247,097.   Patented Sept. 13, 1881.

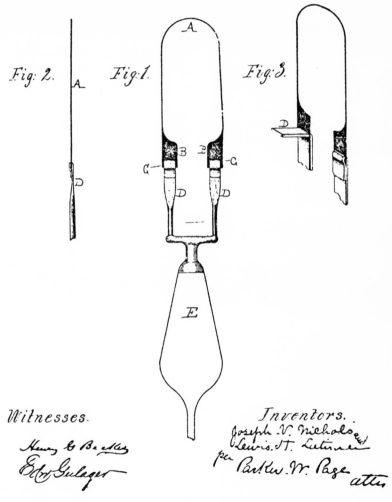

Fig: 2.   Fig: 1.   Fig: 3.

Witnesses.   Inventors.

Latimer's improved method of bonding the filament to the lead wires. (*Courtesy of United States Department of Commerce*)

munity affairs. For a while, he taught at the Henry Street
Settlement House in New York. He was also an accomplished amateur poet. A volume of his poems, privately
published in Italy, is illustrated with pictures of his wife
and three daughters. Most of the poems in the collection
can be described as love poems, and there is no doubt that
they were written for his wife, Mary, to whom he was very
devoted. One poem, in particular, seems to sum up his views
of the difficulties he encountered in his career, and his general philosophy:

LOVE IS ALL

What is there in this world, beside
  our loves
To keep us here?
Ambition's course is paved with
  hopes deferred
With doubt and fear
Wealth brings no joy
And brazen throated fame,
Leaves us at last
Nought but an empty name
O soul, receive the truth
E'er heaven sends thy recall
Nought here deserves our thought
  but love
For love is all

Latimer's writing was not limited to poetry. In 1890 he
wrote a book on electricity, *Incandescent Electric Lighting,
A Practical Description of the Edison System.* The book
was published by the D. Van Nostrand Company of New
York and sold quite a few copies.

He continued to invent, and in his inventive activities

he did not limit himself to electrical devices. In 1886 he received a patent on something he called "apparatus for cooling and disinfecting." Refrigeration was in its infancy then, but apparently Latimer felt it would some day be in great demand. He was unable to follow up this invention due to lack of capital. In 1896 he patented a device for locking hats, coats, and umbrellas on hanging racks, and in 1905 he invented a new type of book support.

After the Edison-Westinghouse patent control board was dissolved in 1911, Latimer worked for Erwin Hammer, a New York City engineer. Shortly afterwards he was back in the kind of work that had started it all. He became associated with the patent attorney firm of Hammer and Schwarz. Hammer had also worked for Edison. Hammer gathered a collection of incandescent lamps, and this collection, which includes Latimer's lamp, is now on exhibit in a museum in Detroit.

In 1918 a group of men who had been associated with Edison formed an organization called The Edison Pioneers. To qualify for membership, a man had to have been involved with Edison during the inventor's creative period. Latimer was a charter member and was present at the meeting when the organization was officially set up.

Latimer continued in the active employ of Hammer and Schwarz until 1924 when a serious illness forced his retirement. He died at his home in Flushing, New York, on December 11, 1928. The Edison Pioneers published an obituary in their official publication which was headed by the following:

> We hardly mourn his inevitable going so much as we rejoice in pleasant memory at having associated with him in a great work for all peoples under a great man . . .

The obituary also included:

> . . . He was of the colored race, the only one in our organization, and was one of those to respond to the initial call that led to the formation of the Edison Pioneers, January 24, 1918. Broadmindedness, versatility in the accomplishment of things intellectual and cultural, a linguist, a devoted husband and father, all were characteristic of him, and his genial presence will be missed from our gatherings . . .

According to his wish, his remains were cremated and placed in the same grave with his wife in the cemetery at Fall River, Massachusetts.

On November 9, 1929, the fiftieth anniversary of Edison's invention of the incandescent lamp was celebrated in a series of observances called "Light's Golden Jubilee." One of the ceremonies was held at Edison's West Orange, New Jersey, laboratories. Latimer's two daughters attended, and their presence was noted in several news reports of the observances. On the occasion of the seventy-fifth anniversary celebration in 1954, Latimer was not mentioned, nor were any members of his family present.

On May 10, 1968, the memory of Lewis Latimer was honored by the dedication of a public school in Brooklyn, New York, called the Lewis H. Latimer School. Two of his grandchildren, Gerald and Winifred Norman, were present at the ceremony, and they presented the school with a portrait of Latimer. The original picture of the founding members of the Edison Pioneers can be seen at the Edison National Historical Site in West Orange, New Jersey.

THROUGH SMOKE, FUMES, AND TRAFFIC

The man who would be an inventor chooses a quixotic way of life. A nine-to-five job in an office or factory is far more secure than the inventor's unpredictable windmill of fortune that can lift him to great heights or dash him into the dust. Garrett A. Morgan chose the uncertain life of the inventor, and although his life had far more excitement and activity than he would have had in a prosaic job, his choice was all the more perilous for the age in which he lived. For at the time when Morgan started to invent, men such as he were about to become a thing of the past.

By the beginning of the twentieth century, technology and science were approaching the point where they are today; a time in which a man without specialized education is defeated before he even starts. Thomas Edison discovered this fact of life all too painfully as the empire he built outgrew him. The twentieth-century inventor is most frequently a man with advanced degrees in the employ of a corporation. His inventions are often assigned to the corporation which has the resources to manufacture and promote them. By the beginning of this century, the independent inventor of the "Yankee Tinkerer" tradition was hard pressed to find the means to promote his inventions, even if he did succeed in obtaining patents. In spite of the problems of no education, no connections, and being black, Garrett Morgan succeeded in an age in which he was supposed to be obsolete.

Garrett Morgan, born in 1877, was one of eleven children of Sydney and Elizabeth Reed Morgan. He was born in Paris, Kentucky, a town in the poor, mountainous, eastern region of that state, and there were few opportunities for education or any kind of advancement for anyone, much less for a black man. Morgan had to leave school after the fifth grade, and at the age of fourteen he left the Kentucky mountains and went across the Ohio River to Cincinnati where he found a job as a handy man. But Garret Morgan did not leave Kentucky to be a handy man, and in Cincinnati, which was very southern in character, there seemed to be no future. So in 1895 he went to Cleveland, broke but still hopeful.

Morgan got a job as a sewing machine mechanic, and in the next few years worked for a number of companies in the sewing machine business. He carefully saved his money, and by 1907 he had started his own sewing machine business: an auspicious start, remembering that the Wright brothers had started out in Ohio in a bicycle shop. Morgan did well and was able to buy a home for himself and his bride after only one year in business.

One of Morgan's most profitable enterprises came about as a result of an accident similar to the discoveries of Goodyear's rubber vulcanization process and Ehrlich's bacteria stains: Goodyear had accidentally spilled a rubber-sulphur mixture on a stove and usable rubber resulted; Ehrlich left some of his slides on a room heater and the

Garrett A. Morgan as a young man. (*Courtesy of Garrett A. Morgan, Jr.*)

heat proved to be what was needed to cause the bacteria on the slide to take up the color of the stain.

Morgan's lucky accident stemmed from a problem he had encountered in running a clothing manufacturing business he had started in 1909. The problem was that the needles on the sewing machines moved so rapidly that the resulting heat of friction caused scorching of some types of fabrics, such as woolens. Morgan experimented with various lubricating materials, and in the course of an evening's experimentation, having just been called to dinner, he wiped his hands on a piece of coarse, wiry pony fur that happened to be close by. Upon his return, he found that the pony fur was straight and pliable. Morgan applied the material to a neighbor's terrier dog, and the dog's normally wiry hair became so straight that he looked like a different dog. (No harm resulted to the dog.)

Morgan incorporated the material into a petroleum jelly base and marketed it as a cosmetic hair straightening preparation. The hair straightener can hardly be described as a significant invention. But its profitability made it possible for Morgan to devote most of his time to inventing. He founded the G. A. Morgan Hair Refining Company and promoted his product with extensive advertising. The company is still in business and thriving.

Morgan's inventive activity took a new direction following his success with the hair preparation. He had developed an interest in safety devices. He was concerned with the frequent instances of firemen being overcome by thick smoke when they had to enter burning buildings. Morgan saw the need for a simple, dependable means of protecting firemen and other workers from the effects of smoke and harmful fumes.

At the time, a variety of devices consisting of tanks of

G. A. MORGAN.
BREATHING DEVICE
APPLICATION FILED AUG. 19, 1912.

1,113,675.

Patented Oct. 13, 1914.
2 SHEETS—SHEET 1.

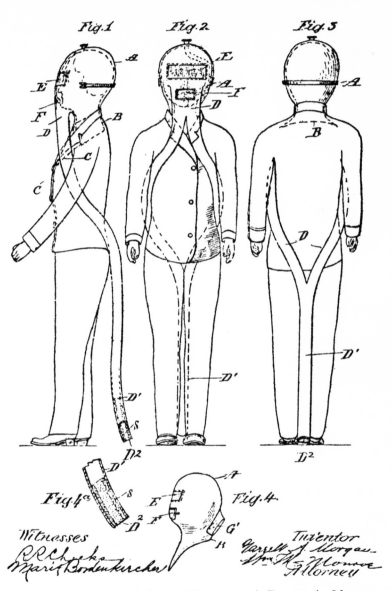

Morgan's first safety helmet. (*Courtesy of Garrett A. Morgan, Jr.*)

air, tubes, and complicated valve systems were in use. Many of these required constant adjustment while in use, and valves would sometimes stick in open or closed position at the most inopportune times. Many of the respirator devices were so undependable that it was standard procedure to send at least two firemen at a time into a smoky situation, so that one could aid the other in case his respirator broke down.

Morgan started work on what he called a "breathing device" in 1910, and in 1912 he felt he had perfected it to the point where he could apply for a patent, which was granted on October 13, 1914. The device was amazing in its simplicity. It consisted of a canvas hood that was placed over the head. From the hood a double tube extended and merged into a single tube at the back of the wearer. The open end was fitted with a sponge that was moistened with water to serve as a trap for smoke particles and to cool the air which entered the tube. A metal tube inside the hood ran from the mouth of the user to a ball valve at the top of the hood. When the user exhaled, the force of air raised the ball from its seat so that the exhalation could escape. When the user inhaled, the ball was drawn tightly against the seat and the smoke was prevented from entering the hood. The ball-and-seat valve is the simplest type of valve, and it was the only moving part of the device. There was nothing that could break down. Morgan even thought to provide ear channels so the user could hear what was going on around him.

The operation of the device rested on a basic physical principle. Heated air tends to rise and carry smoke to the ceiling. So, in a smoky room, a layer of nearly smokeless air tends to accumulate near the floor. The large tube extending from Morgan's breathing device enabled the user to draw on this layer of relatively clean air. The device was versatile. The tube could be extended out of a window or directed upward if there was a thermal inversion that resulted in smokeless air at the top of the room rather than at the bottom. The device was later modified to carry its own air supply, and this modification had great significance on the battlefields of World War I.

Morgan had learned a great deal about product promotion from his experience with the hair straightener. He formed a company, The National Safety Device Company, and advertised extensively in firemen's magazines; he drew on testimonials from satisfied users which he incorporated into direct-mail advertising brochures. He staged spectacular demonstrations of the device, and newspaper coverage of these demonstrations proved to be the most valuable kind of advertising. Morgan traveled extensively to personally demonstrate his invention to fire departments all over the country.

The National Safety Device Company was set up as a corporation and stock in the company was offered for sale. The invention was marketed as the Morgan National Safety Hood. Morgan himself did not own a majority of stock, but he was the general manager of the corporation and, of course, received royalties on sales. He made an effort to encourage blacks to buy stock in the company, but he was unsuccessful. In less than five years the stock increased in value from ten dollars a share to $250.

The hood was adopted by Akron, Ohio, a rubber-manu- facturing center with a potential for fires of a particularly noxious variety. And fires were indeed frequent in Akron's rubber factories. J. T. Metz, Akron fire chief in the 1910s, made a practice of carrying a couple of Morgan's safety hoods in his car along with a supply of hand fire extinguishers. He was frequently the first to arrive at a fire and on many occasions he had the fire out before the apparatus arrived. Even the smallest fire in a rubber factory tends to produce the most awful kind of smoke. But Chief Metz would don the hood, go into the building with a hand extinguisher and a powerful flashlight and put out the fire before it had a chance to spread. The hood made this technique possible. Chief Metz worte:

> . . . What is the use of fighting fires all night when you can do the work in fifteen minutes? Two men equipped with the Morgan helmet and a good fire extinguisher can accomplish more in fifteen minutes than a whole company can in the next thirty minutes. . . . I have used the Morgan helmet in my department for over a year and it has given me great satisfaction in assisting me in saving human lives and property, and I am sure it has saved our city many thousand dollars . . .

Morgan preferred to personally demonstrate his device whenever possible. He thought it advisable, for obvious reasons, to employ white men to carry out demonstrations in southern cities. One such demonstration in New Orleans was of particular interest and was reported in the New Orleans *Times-Picayune* of October 22, 1914. A tent was constructed and a fire fueled by tar, sulfur, formaldehyde, and manure was started in the confines of the tent. The smell of the smoke of this fire had to be experienced to be fully appreciated. The climax of the demonstration, conducted by Charles P. Salan, former director of public works for Cleveland, occurred when "Big Chief Mason," who according to the newspaper story was a "full-blooded Indian from the Walpole Reservation, Canada," entered the smoke-filled tent wearing the safety hood and remained there for twenty minutes with no apparent ill effect. The story went on to describe the safety device but contained no further mention of "Big Chief Mason," who was no Indian but none other than Garrett Morgan. Morgan felt that adoption of his invention by a city as large and important as New Orleans was a vital one and he wanted to be there to see that the demonstration went well. And perhaps drawing on the experience of Norbert Rillieux some seventy-five years earlier, thought it best not to reveal to the New Orleans officials that the safety hood was the product of a black man. Morgan also used the Big Chief Mason guise on other occasions.

The most spectacular demonstration of the capabilities of the safety hood, and the one that made its inventor known all over the country, was not planned by Morgan, and it occurred in his home town of Cleveland.

In 1916 a tunnel was being constructed under Lake Erie for the Cleveland Water Works. On the night of July 25, 1916, there was an explosion in a section of this tunnel called "Crib Number 5." After three rescue parties entered the tunnel and failed to return, no one else had the courage to enter the tunnel for further rescue attempts. At this point Morgan was called to the scene. Awakened at 3 A.M., he did not even take time to dress. He arrived at the scene barefoot and clad only in a pair of pajama bottoms. But he brought several of his safety hoods. A tugboat took him to the scene of the disaster where he was met by the mayor, policemen, and firemen, all of whom had refused to enter the tunnel. Morgan, his brother, and two other volunteers donned safety hoods and went down the shaft into the tunnel. In their haste they forgot to take a flashlight.

Upon entering the tunnel they almost immediately came across the dead body of one of the victims. The man had died with a flashlight in his hands. Morgan took the flash-

Morgan's National Safety Hood

Style Two Helmet

Combination Smoke, Gas, Ammonia and Sand Blast Protector.

Safety helmet modified to carry own air supply; basis of gas mask. (*Courtesy of Garrett A. Morgan, Jr.*)

light and led the party deeper into the tunnel. They found
the superintendent of the tunnel project who was not breathing but was still alive. When he was brought to the surface
the police wanted to use a pulmotor on him. A pulmotor is
a device which forcibly drives air into and out of the lungs.
Morgan would not allow the pulmotor to be used, expressing
fear that it might rupture the victim's lungs. Morgan applied
artificial respiration and the victim was revived. Morgan's
fear of the pulmotor has been shown to be correct, and the
device is no longer widely used.

Morgan went down into the tunnel many more times.
When it was seen that Morgan and the other volunteers
emerged safely, other men joined in the rescue effort
and many of the workers were saved.

The wire services picked up the story and accounts of
Morgan's heroism appeared in newspapers all over the country. He was awarded a medal by a Cleveland citizen's group
and a medal from the International Association of Fire
Engineers, which also made him an honorary member. As
a result of the publicity, orders for Morgan's safety hood
increased dramatically. However, the publicity had a reverse effect in some parts of the country. The newspaper
stories made it known that the inventor of the safety hood
was black and orders from many cities, especially those in
the South, all but stopped.

Andrew Carnegie had endowed the Carnegie Hero Fund
Commission to reward people who carried out heroic deeds.
Thomas A. Farrell, Cleveland's Director of Public Utilities,
wrote a letter to the Commission in 1917 in which he
described Morgan's rescue efforts in the crib disaster and
proposed that he be honored by the fund as a hero. A great
deal of correspondence followed, and the action of the Commission was rather curious. They awarded their hero medal

not to Morgan but to Mr. C. Van Husen, the project super-intendent whose life Morgan had saved. The Commission concluded that what Morgan did was "not beyond the call of duty." This decision was difficult to understand since Morgan was not a fireman or policeman, but a private citizen who was under no obligation to risk his life and did so only when firemen and policemen had refused, out of fear, to carry out their duty. The whole affair smacked of racism on the part of some members of the Commission.

Morgan's invention continued to enjoy success as it was adopted by fire departments all over the country and found use in many industrial applications where fumes and dust of various types were frequently problems. At the Second International Exposition of Safety and Sanitation, held in New York in 1914, Morgan's invention had been awarded "First Grand Prize," winning out over hundreds of safety

A better protection for the pedestrian, sch

G. A. ▓▓▓▓ Morgan Safet

5202 Harlem Avenue

devices on exhibit at the convention. A more practical testimonial than gold medals was awarded when the safety hoods were removed from the exhibition booth and used by New York firemen to rescue victims of a subway accident.

Events on a World War I battlefield were to provide a tragic new use for Morgan's safety hood. The Second Battle of Ypres was considered to be particularly important by both the Germans and the Allies. During April and May of 1915 the Germans desperately attempted to break through at this Flanders town, and the British were equally as desperate to stop them, for if the Germans broke through they would probably have taken the ports of Calais and Dunkirk. The loss of these ports would have been a serious blow to the Allied war effort. Unable to make any headway against the British Army, the Germans introduced a new weapon they had been saving for just such an occasion—chlorine gas.

ildren and R.R. crossing

Advertising brochure for traffic signal; the partnership with Sands did not last long. (*Courtesy of Garrett A. Morgan, Jr.*)

em

Cleveland, Ohio

can Patents Allowed, Foreign Patents Pending

The British troops were scattered by the choking clouds of the greenish gas, but the Germans failed to follow through on this victory achieved by the first known use of poison gas in warfare.

The British needed a defense against poison gas and they needed it in a hurry. They turned to Morgan's safety hood; the model that carried its own air supply. Morgan's device, as it existed in 1915, proved to be too bulky for battlefield use, but it saved many lives until more compact models based on Morgan's principles could be developed. When the United States entered the war gas masks based on Morgan's principles were used by the American Army, and by the German Army too, as the use of poison gas became commonplace on the World War I battlefields. After the Americans entered the war, Morgan demonstrated his safety hood to the Navy for use on submarines.

Morgan was now committed to inventions for safety, and his next efforts were directed at doing something about the chaos that ever-increasing numbers of automobiles were bringing about on the streets and highways. Accidents were particularly frequent in cities, especially at intersections. In some cities policemen were stationed at the busier intersections, as they are today, but it was impossible to have a policeman at every intersection. Many traffic-control schemes were tried. One of the more interesting and somewhat bizarre efforts at traffic control was in Philadelphia where a revolving light was placed at the top of City Hall, then the tallest building in the city. When the light faced in a north-south direction all drivers moving in that direction were supposed to stop; and, similarly, when the light faced in an east-west direction. Of course it was impossible for all drivers to see the light, and many who did ignored it anyway. This particular attempt at traffic control did not last very long.

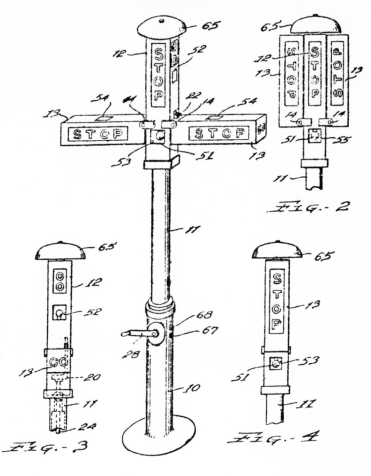

Nov. 20 , 1923.

G. A. MORGAN

TRAFFIC SIGNAL

Filed Feb. 27. 1922

1,475,024

2 Sheets—Sheet 1

FIG.- 2

FIG.- 3

FIG.- 1

FIG.- 4

INVENTOR
Garrett A. Morgan,
By Baker & Macklin,
ATTORNEYS

Morgan's traffic signal. (*Courtesy of Garrett A. Morgan, Jr.*)

Garrett Morgan at an exhibit of his inventions; Morgan died a few weeks after this picture was taken. (*Jim Gayle, Courtesy of Garrett A. Morgan, Jr.*)

Morgan developed a traffic signal and received a patent for the device on November 20, 1923. It was made up of semaphore arms that could be raised, lowered, and revolved in a variety of ways to direct traffic in many different situations. It was equipped with a warning bell and with lights for nighttime use. It was more effective and versatile than any system in use at the time and was widely used until replaced by the familiar automatically timed electric signals in use today. Morgan made a brief attempt to market the invention himself, but later sold it to the General Electric Company for forty thousand dollars. Morgan's device is generally regarded as the first true traffic-control signal.

Morgan maintained an active interest in many fields besides invention. In the 1920s he and others started a newspaper, the Cleveland *Call*. This newspaper is still published as the Cleveland *Call and Post*. With Cincinnati and Columbus editions, it has one of the largest circulations of any black newspaper in the midwest.

Morgan did not allow his lack of education to interfere with an interest in academic affairs. He was concerned with the education of black youth, especially at Cleveland's Western Reserve University. He was instrumental in organizing a fraternity of black students at this school. The preliminary organizational meetings were held at his home, and he helped in many other ways, including financial.

In 1953, on the occasion of the thirty-eighth anniversary of the founding of the fraternity, Morgan, the inventor with the fifth-grade education, and Thurgood Marshall were honored together at a testimonial banquet. At the time, Marshall was presenting the case against school segregation to the Supreme Court, the same body on which he serves today as an Associate Justice. The President of Western Reserve University, Charles Thwing, once said of Morgan, ". . . a great Clevelander, one who has achieved greatness because he was willing to dig, and in spite of his limited education."

Morgan was active in the Cleveland Association of Colored Men, a precursor of the NAACP in that city. He remained an active, contributing member after the group became part of the NAACP. In 1967, at the Shrine National Convention in Cleveland, a stainless-steel plaque bearing an etched likeness of Morgan was dedicated and mounted on a marble pillar in the Hall of Fame of the Cleveland Public Auditorium.

Morgan had glaucoma, and by the mid-1940s the disease had progressed to the point where he had less than 10 per cent vision. But he remained active, and only a few weeks before his death he attended a special exhibition of his inventions.

He died on July 27, 1963, shortly before he planned to attend the Emancipation Centennial Celebration in Chicago where he was to be honored as a man who beat the odds and was successful as an independent inventor in the twentieth century.

The Old Cotton Fields Back Home

Although the rapidly expanding post-Civil War economy was primarily industrial, the nation's agriculture was also, to a large extent, "industrialized" during this period. New farm machinery, chemical fertilizers, and scientific farming methods dramatically increased yields per acre. Meat production was mechanized, and the railroads carred the products of the big meat packers of Omaha, Kansas City, and Chicago to all parts of the nation.

While most of the country's agriculture prospered, the potentially productive fields of the South lay dormant and its people were destitute. Southerners could easily put the blame for their troubles on losing the war, but the unproductive state of southern farms would have come about in any case, war or no war, win or lose. True, the railroads had been torn up, and the plantation houses were burned, but crops were never grown on the railroad tracks or in the manor houses. The war itself had done nothing to the soil. The destruction of southern agriculture had come from the southern system itself, a system that centered about slavery and cotton. Losing the war just made it harder to correct the blunders of the past.

The invention of the cotton gin had assured that the agriculture of the deep South would be almost exclusively devoted to cotton. Cotton, however, is well known as a destroyer of soil. The plant draws practically all the nutrients and returns none of it back to the soil. In the early days of cotton culture, the cotton fields were moved South and West as old fields were worn out. Red, dusty, abandoned fields and decaying houses were common sights in the South.

Cotton culture was profitable only when grown on large plantations and attended by legions of unpaid slaves. The supply of land was not limitless, and the cotton kingdom was doomed before it started. When the war had ended, slavery was gone and the big plantations were broken up. Cotton had already ruined the land, but the Southerners stuck with cotton because it was a cash crop, and more significantly, because it was a habit they did not know how to break.

The pieces of the plantations were parceled out to former slaves in keeping with the "Forty Acres and a Mule" concept. The small farmers planted their acres in cotton right up to the doorstep of their cabins. Many never bothered to even plant a vegetable garden trusting that the cash from cotton would buy their sustenance. But the worn-out soil yielded little, and what little money that was earned had to go for fertilizer if one was to hope for a crop the next year.

The small farmer just could not make it, and many became tenants or "sharecroppers" on large spreads of land. So the demands of cotton culture resulted in somewhat the same situation that had existed before the war; in large spreads of land worked by legions of black bodies. But there was one significant modification: many of the share-croppers were white.

The sharecropper paid his rent to the owner in a portion of the crop. He was free to sell the rest. The sharecropping system resulted in a new kind of slavery. The sharecroppers, for the most part, continued to refuse to grow food crops for their own use and, therefore, fell into debt to the landowner and local merchants for their food and other needs. They could not leave the land as long as they were in debt, and they were as surely slaves as some of them had been before 1863.

The landowners were themselves slaves to the pseudo agriculture of hearsay, superstition, and ingrained habit that was cotton culture. The dead soil was nothing more than a receptacle for the tons of guano and other fertilizer that had to be bought with the meager proceeds of last year's crop. Many cotton farmers paid more heed to such dogmas as "sowing when the moon was right" than to matters of proper depth of furrow or rotation of crops. When the seed was sown there was nothing else to do but sit back and see what would happen. The weeds had to be "chopped" once or twice, and praying for enough rain and hoping that the weevils wouldn't eat up the crop, was the extent of the cotton farmer's activities until picking time—if there was anything to pick when the season had run its course. As the years went on from Reconstruction into the 1880s and 1890s, the situation did not improve. Something or someone dramatic and miraculous was needed to shake the Southern farmer out of the one-crop folly.

GEORGE WASHINGTON CARVER

George Washington Carver looked neither dramatic nor miraculous. Someone seeing him for the first time would be more likely to describe him as "funny-looking." One person who knew him said that when he stood up he looked like a question mark. His poor posture and slightly bent appearance were the legacy of a sickly infancy and precarious survival into childhood. But Carver survived, and what he accomplished in his lifetime was nothing short of miraculous. Men with far more physical stamina than George Carver would have given up at any number of points along the way he traveled from his birth as a slave to his achievement at Tuskegee. He, more than any one person, showed the southern farmer the way out of the cotton nightmare.

George Washington Carver was born of slave parents in Missouri in 1860. At the time, Missouri was in a state of almost complete anarchy. Pitched battles were fought between free-soil and slavery men from neighboring Kansas. The area was also plagued with marauding bands who held to no particular ideology other than the personal one of stealing whatever they could. A band of these marauders stole the infant George and his mother, Mary, in a swift night raid on the farm of Moses Carver, George's owner.

Moses Carver was a reluctant slaveholder. He had bought Mary only because he and his wife could not handle the farm without help. Mary was considered to be part of the family, and when she and the baby were stolen, Moses hired a local "bushwhacker" of questionable character, but possessed of great tracking skill, to find them. The bushwhacker failed to find Mary but he found George, who had been left for dead by the raiders. Moses gave the bushwhacker a fine race horse in payment of services rendered. Moses and Sue Carver had no children of their own and George and his brother, Jim, were raised as the Carver's own children.

George was a frail, sickly boy, unable to do much heavy work on the farm. Even as a child, he exhibited a persistent curiosity and a remarkable talent for making things grow. He, of course, wanted to go to school, but there were the usual insurmountable obstacles facing a black child who wished for education. There were no schools for black children in the immediate vicinity of the Carver farm, so the young boy made a rather brave, seemingly foolhardly decision to leave the security of the Carver's farm and strike out alone to look for a school.

Carver's personal odyssey lasted for well over twenty-five years before he came to Tuskegee. During his travels he worked at various jobs, ran a laundry, and even tried homesteading. He picked up whatever bits of schooling he could, wherever he found a classroom he could enter. He stayed with a number of families and in many instances paid for his keep by working as a domestic. One of these families took him to Minneapolis, Kansas, where he attended a high school. Despite his sketchy primary education, he did well in the high school and sent off an application to

Highland College, a small Presbyterian school in Kansas, where he was accepted. But when he turned up at the college to register, he was promptly told to leave as soon as they saw that he was black.

He remained in Highland after the humiliating rejection simply because he had no money to go anywhere else. He worked as a cook until he had enough money to leave the place and to go homesteading in Kansas. He built his sod house, planted crops, and tried to forget. He could not stand the stagnation of this life for very long, and he pulled up stakes again and went to Winterset, Iowa. In that town he was befriended by a white family, the Millhollands, who encouraged him to try college again. He was accepted at Simpson College in Iowa and not turned away when he got there. He was thirty years old when he started his freshman year.

Carver arrived at the campus penniless and promptly set up a laundry business. The laundry brought in enough for food and books. At Simpson he developed an interest in art, which never left him. He wanted to go to Paris to study art and make a career of it. He loved painting and his decision to study agriculture rather than art was a very painful one for him to make.

In 1891 Carver enrolled at the Iowa State College of Agriculture and Mechanic Arts at Ames (now Iowa State College). The college at Ames had already achieved some fame as a producer of leaders of American Agriculture. Three Secretaries of Agriculture, James G. Wilson, Henry C. Wallace, and his son, Henry A. Wallace, went to Iowa State. Henry A. Wallace was Vice-President of the United States under Franklin D. Roosevelt from 1941 to 1945. As a small boy, he frequently accompanied Carver on botanizing trips, and the two of them became lifelong friends.

Carver attended Ames for four years and earned his Bachelor of Science degree in 1894. He painted whenever he could. One of his paintings was awarded an honorable mention at the Chicago World's Columbian Exposition in 1893. When he graduated he was offered a graduate assistantship in botany at the Ames Agricultural Experiment Station under Dr. Pammell, a leading botanist of the time. Dr. Pammell thought highly of Carver, and Carver wrote several professional papers. He seemed well on his way to an academic career in botany, concentrating on fungal diseases of plants, when he received his Master's degree in 1896.

Just as Carver was completing his Master's work, he received a letter from Booker T. Washington, the head of Tuskegee Normal and Industrial Institute in Alabama. Washington invited Carver to take a position as head of the new Agriculture Department. Carver had made a place for himself in the warm, friendly, academic atmosphere at Ames. He was reluctant to leave, but he felt that he had to accept Washington's offer. In his reply to Washington he wrote:

> . . . of course it has always been the one great ideal of my life to be of the greatest good to the greatest number of "my people" possible, and to this end I have been preparing myself for these many years; feeling as I do that this line of education is the key to unlock the golden door of freedom to our people.

Tuskegee Institute had been set up as a school for training black teachers in 1880 when Negroes still had some political power in Alabama. Even after all political power passed to the whites, Washington managed to wheedle additional, modest appropriations from the white men in the Alabama legislature. It was one such appropriation, for an agricultural department in the Institute, that opened the way for Carver to come to Tuskegee at a salary of fifteen hundred dollars a year. Funds for the buildings had been provided by northern philanthropists.

The intensity and complexity of the southern racial syndrome was a new experience for Carver. True, he had experienced some of the inevitable trauma of being black in America, such as his cruel rejection from Highland, and in a small town in Kansas he had witnessed a particularly brutal lynching of a black man. Much of his life, however, had been spent in close friendship with white families and in the sheltered academic community at Ames. He had come to ignore the stares, the slurring remarks, and the many other indignities visited upon him by the anonymous white world, but he was not quite prepared for what he came across in Alabama.

Tuskegee was an all-black enclave in the white supremacist stronghold of Alabama. The whites tolerated Tuskegee and left it alone. But the students and faculty were expected to abide by the intricate web of unwritten "rules and regulations" of black subservience when they were in town. Even Booker T. Washington felt it the better part of valor to attach the caboose of a "sir" to any statement directed to a white man. It was a strange, contradictory, incomprehensible world to anyone not born into it. It was a world in which a black could prepare food for a white but not eat at the same table or drink from the same fountain. Carver found that a black man might be called "Professor" or "Doctor" by a white man but never "Mister." Carver narrowly missed being lynched on one occasion when he violated one of the sanctities of the system by riding in a wagon in which a white woman sat in the front seat next to the black driver. It was in this world that Carver did his

George Washington Carver in his Tuskegee laboratory. (*Courtesy of Tuskegee Institute*)

great work and showed the way to a better life for all people of the South—black and white.

In connection with his duties as head of the Agriculture Department, he was made director and consulting chemist of the agricultural experiment station and instructor in scientific agriculture and dairy science. Carver knew, before he got to Tuskegee, that merely standing in front of a classroom of students and passing on what he had learned at Iowa was not going to be enough to straighten out the mess in the South. New methods of scientific agriculture directly applicable to the southern agricultural situation had to be researched, and these new methods had to be carried out and shown to the people who were in need of them. Over the years Tuskegee graduates carried Carver's message out to the countryside. He conducted a "Farmer's Institute" for farmers in the area and rigged up a wagon as a mobile demonstration station.

The one-crop system was the most obvious evil, but Carver knew he would come across resistance to any suggestion that cotton not be planted every year. Knowing the dependence on cotton, Carver spent some time developing new strains of cotton that were resistant to disease and produced more bolls per plant. Suspicion came not only from surrounding farmers but from some people within the Institute. He was mistrusted as a theoretical scientist and, oddly enough, as a "Yankee."

Carver has been criticized for his kitchen approach to research problems. He was, however, in a situation where solutions to critical problems were needed in a hurry. Practical applications had to take precedence over pure research. Carver was certainly capable of carrying out pure research, and he thoroughly enjoyed it when he had the chance. Despite the pressures of the necessity of doing mostly applied science, he found time to do some original mycological work on various parasitic fungi.

A visitor to Carver's lab in the early days at Tuskegee would have found it to be more like a kitchen than the common concept of a laboratory. Money was always in short supply and Carver became expert in making do with whatever was available. Why spend money on an Erlenmeyer flask, he said, when a glass jug would do just as well? Carver collected every bottle, can, scrap of wood, metal, and bit of string that might be of some use in his laboratory. He even converted the Institute's waste paper, rags, and other assorted trash into fertilizer by instructing students to discard all such refuse into a pit that had been set aside as a compost heap. When this material rotted it made an excellent fertilizer.

Rotted paper and rags could not solve the great problem of the barren soil that had been drained by cotton. Commercial fertilizers were expensive, and few of the farmers in the region owned enough animals to produce manure in sufficient quantities. Carver's solution to the problem was to plant legumes such as peas, soybeans, and peanuts. These plants enter into a mutualistic relationship with certain soil bacteria that are able to convert atmospheric nitrogen into the soluble nitrates essential for plant growth. The bacteria exist in close association with the plant in little bumps on the roots called nodules. The nitrates, deposited in the soil by the activity of the bacteria, are taken up into the plant through the roots. Commercial fertilizers are nothing more than nitrates, and planting legumes is certainly cheaper than buying fertilizer.

Carver tried to spread the legume doctrine throughout the countryside. He knew it was impossible to completely abandon cotton, which was the only available cash crop.

The most he could do was to encourage crop rotation—planting part of the land in cotton and part in cowpeas, soybeans, peanuts, or some other legume. Even this was difficult, for the farmers needed every penny they could get from cotton. And they had the problem of what to do with the legumes once they had grown them. Carver issued various pamphlets on such topics as how to cook cowpeas, and how legumes were good for animal feed. But these were of limited use. The major problem was that legumes just did not bring in immediate money. There was no market, so Carver turned his attention to creating a market, and the focus of his attention was the peanut. The soybean was more versatile, but the farmers were not familiar with it. The peanut, however, was an old friend.

Carver did not introduce the peanut to the South. It had been known for a long time as the "goober peas" that children enjoyed eating. Many farmers grew a bush or two for their children. To many Confederate veterans, the goober pea was a bad joke. In the latter stages of the war, large numbers of Confederate soldiers subsisted entirely on peanuts, and a popular soldier's song included the words:

> Peas! peas! peas! peas!
> Eatin' goober peas!
> Goodness how "delicious"
> Eatin' goober peas!

Although the Confederate soldiers may have complained of a daily diet of goober peas, the peanuts on which, according to the song, they "grinded off their molars" supplied them with almost as much protein as they would have obtained from a diet that included one meat meal a day. Eating peanuts no doubt saved many a sharecropper's or small farmer's child from a host of dietary deficiency diseases.

Many farmers who had grown peanuts at Carver's advice found themselves with bushels of them, which they could not sell. There was just no market for huge quantities of peanuts. (The problem was so serious that many reverted to the one-crop cotton culture.) Carver felt he was responsible for the situation, and he intensified his efforts to make a market for peanuts. In the late 1890s he carried out careful chemical analyses of peanuts and then proceeded to reassemble the chemical components into a wide variety of new products. From peanuts, Carver produced various oils, a palatable milk, milk products such as cheese, hand and face creams, inks, instant coffees and other food products, ointments, and synthetic rubber, to name a few.

Southern peanut men had organized themselves into an organization called the United Peanut Associations of America in an effort to expand the scope of the peanut business. Some twenty years elapsed between the time Carver started his peanut research and when the Peanut Association men heard about him and his work. The Peanut Association's knowledge of Carver was rather casual. One of their members remarked at a meeting about "some old colored man" in Alabama who had done some rather remarkable things with peanuts. Over the objections of some of the peanut men, Carver was invited to come to a meeting in Montgomery to make a presentation. So Carver took his seat in a Jim Crow railroad car and made the journey to Montgomery.

Carver willingly made the trip, even though travel in the South was frequently a perilous undertaking for a black man, and experienced a good many annoyances and humiliations, all of which he endured silently. The doorman at the hotel where the meeting was held refused to admit him. Finally, Carver persuaded the doorman to deliver a note, and he was led in through a back door and allowed upstairs on a service elevator.

It was this kind of passive submission to the system that earned Carver and Washington a great deal of criticism from the followers of W. E. B. DuBois and others who urged a more militant stand against the white establishment. Carver seldom, if ever, made public statements on the politics of white supremacy and the oppression of blacks. Many felt he was in a position to take a more active stand and that he was shirking his responsibility in refusing to do so. Carver, perhaps, felt a different kind of responsibility. He could have refused to submit to the humiliations he had to endure in order to attend the Peanut Association meeting. But in so refusing he would have missed an opportunity to better the lives of his people by promoting new markets for peanuts. Perhaps he felt that the gaining of economic power was a necessary prerequisite to the gaining of what is today called Black Power.

Carver made his presentation to the peanut men, and they were so impressed that they asked him to testify before the House Ways and Means Committee, which was considering a tariff bill. At the time, peanuts imported from the Far East were providing stiff competition for American-grown peanuts. The Peanut Association wanted the duty raised on imported peanuts. They hoped that Carver's demonstration of the many peanut products he had developed would convince the committee that the peanut was worthy of their consideration.

So in January of 1921 Carver went to Washington, D.C. Carver was no stranger to Washington—in 1918 he had gone there to demonstrate the usefulness of the sweet potato as a substitute for wheat to Army bakers and other food people. He had been given only ten minutes to speak, and it was late in the afternoon before the committee got to him and they were tired and wanted to go home.

Carver showed the committee his oils, milk, face cream, etc., and when the ten minutes were up the Congressmen were so fascinated that Congressman Garner of Texas (later to be Vice-President of the United States) moved that Carver's time be extended. The genius from Tuskegee went on for almost two hours and received a standing ovation when he had finished.

The peanut did not command Carver's exclusive interest. In the 1900s he had made useful products from sweet potatoes, pecans, soybeans, cowpeas, and even from Alabama clay. From clay he extracted dyes and color washes. The latter were a cheap substitute for paint and helped to brighten many a shack and cabin. One of his clay pigments, a rich blue, attracted the attention of several paint manufacturers. They all offered rather attractive deals for rights to use the pigments, all of which Carver turned down. At the time, he did not want to become involved in commercial enterprises. Of course the paint manufacturers used the pigments anyway, despite Carver's attempt to protect his discoveries with patents.

Carver, who at times went for months without cashing a pay check, had little need for money. His refusal to make money from his inventions, if not for himself then for the Institute or some other worthy cause, seemed to many to be contradictory to his appeals to black farmers to make and save money for buying their own land. In the 1920s, however, there was an attempt to organize a Carver Products Company to manufacture and promote Carver's peanut and sweet potato products. The company was inadequately capitalized and never advanced beyond the planning stages. Only a very small fraction of the hundreds of products

Carver developed from peanuts, sweet potatoes, clay, and other materials has been utilized on a large commercial scale. And the reason is a matter of economics. The products they were intended to replace are still in abundance so that many of the Carver substitutes cannot compete. Carver once commented that his peanut milk and cheese would never put the cow out of business. However, products of the genius of Carver are available, should the need ever arise. And during the two World Wars, when supplies of various materials were cut off, many of Carver's discoveries proved to be of vital importance.

Paint companies were not the only enterprises interested in Carver. He received job offers from Thomas Edison and Henry Ford, both of whom he turned down. Carver and Ford became close friends and Ford frequently dropped in at Tuskegee. They had many mutual interests, including the development of synthetic rubber from goldenrod. Carver also visited one of Edison's plants in St. Louis. While there he commented that there were no black workers at the plant except those in the furnace rooms and in various custodial jobs. Apparently, no one there knew of Lewis Latimer who was working for Edison at the time.

Carver received many honors in his lifetime, and if any black scientist or inventor would not qualify as a "hidden" contributor, it would be Carver. He was by far the best-known black scientist, and to most whites he was thought of as the "only" black scientist. Among the honors he obtained are the Spingarn Medal awarded by the NAACP "to the man or woman of African descent who will have made the highest achievement . . . in an honorable field of human endeavor" (first awarded to Ernest Just in 1915); honorary doctoral degrees from Simpson College and the University of Rochester; elected a Fellow of the Royal Society of

Arts, Manufactures, and Commerce (Great Britain); the Theodore Roosevelt Medal for distinguished research in agricultural chemistry; chosen "Man of the Year" by the International Federation of Architects, Engineers, Chemists, and Technicians; and, posthumously, he was honored by a joint resolution of Congress, which designated January 5, 1946, as George Washington Carver Day.

The greatest monument to Carver is not medals and scrolls, but the acres of southern fields that were again productive with something other than cotton, and the small farmers, black and white, who found new dignity in owning their own land.

In the few years that he was at Ames, Carver distinguished himself sufficiently to gain some acceptance into the previously all-white scientific "fraternity." The earning of a Ph.D. is prerequisite for admission, and there is no doubt that had he remained at Ames he would have gone on for his doctorate or that, because of his enthusiasm and capacity for work, the botanical journals would have contained many of his papers. His successful entrance into the scientific world was all the more remarkable since he was thirty when he started college, an age when most men embarking on a scientific career have already earned their doctorate degree.

Carver gave up a promising career in pure science so that he could be of service to his people as a practical agricultural scientist. His achievements at Tuskegee were no less remarkable because of his lack of an earned doctorate or the late start forced on him by the brutal racial prejudices that made it so difficult for him to obtain a basic education.

Carver made up for his late start by continuing to work long after the usual retirement age of sixty-five. He remained active until his death in 1943 at the age of eighty-three.

The Healers

The history of man's efforts to heal other men is almost as old as the history of men killing other men. All cultures, civilized or primitive, have had healers—whether they were witch doctors or neurosurgeons. Undoubtedly, healers of various types were in the holds of slave ships, although it seems likely that witch doctors and such may have had enough influence to avoid them.

Slaves were valuable pieces of property and the prudent master could not afford to neglect sickness and injuries. The quality and nature of the treatment, however, varied. Either the slaves were treated by the slaveowner's own physician or veterinarian, or by the slaveowner himself. Some were attended by another slave who was familiar with natural medications or various supernatural techniques of African origin.

When slavery was over the ex-slaves still needed medical treatment, but there were very few doctors who would treat blacks. The few black physicians were in the cities where they had attended to the medical needs of free blacks long before the Civil War. These physicians ranged from compounders of folk medicines to men who had been trained in European universities. This inconsistency in the training of physicians was by no means limited to black doctors but was characteristic of all medicine. As recently as the first decades of this century, it was possible for a man to be a licensed, practicing physician by virtue of a one- or two-year course or even through mail-order training. It was also a common practice to become an apprentice to a physician.

A slave named James Derham, born in Philadelphia in 1762, belonged to physicians during the entire time he was a slave. His first owner was Dr. John Kearsley, who taught him how to compound medicines. He was sold to Dr. George West, a British Army surgeon, from whom he learned more medicine and surgical techniques. His last master was Dr. Robert Dove of New Orleans, from whom Derham bought his freedom in 1783. Shortly afterwards Derham set himself up in practice in New Orleans, and as such, he can be called the first American black physician. Since he had, in effect, been apprenticed to three different physicians, he had benefited from the experience of all of his masters and was one of the best-trained physicians of any color in New Orleans.

Derham had a very successful practice and flourished in pre-Louisiana Purchase New Orleans. He was regarded as one of the most distinguished physicians in New Orleans and is known to have prepared many new medications, including a snake bite remedy. He was visited by Dr. Benjamin Rush, signer of the Declaration of Independence and Surgeon General of the Continental Army, who wrote of Derham:

I have conversed with him upon most of the acute and epidemic diseases of the country where he lives, and was pleased to find him perfectly acquainted with the modern simple mode of practice in these diseases. I expected to have suggested many new medicines to him but he suggested many more to me. He is very modest and engaging in his manners.

THE HEART SURGEON

People have always been intrigued with firsts, such as the first man on the moon or even such inconsequentials as the first person to cross a new bridge. Dr. Daniel Hale Williams, a black physician active in the late nineteenth and early twentieth centuries, is credited with performing the first successful heart surgery. This particular operation was indeed an outstanding feat of surgical skill, but it has tended to detract from the other achievements of this physician who devoted his life to improving the quality of medical care for black Americans.

Daniel Williams, born in 1856, was one of seven children of a barber in a small town in central Pennsylvania. When Dan's father died of tuberculosis in 1867 there was not enough money to hold the family together. So Dan went to Baltimore and was apprenticed to a shoemaker. He never wanted to be a shoemaker, so he ran away and worked at various jobs until he eventually rejoined part of his family in Edgerton, Wisconsin. In Edgerton, he was apprenticed to Harry Anderson, who was a barber. Anderson was also the town bandsman, and Williams played the string bass in one of Anderson's musical groups.

Harry Anderson was a good friend to the young Williams. He sent him to a private school called Haire's Classical Academy, in the nearby town of Janesville. Some of the parents of the students objected to Williams and pressured the principal, John Haire, to dismiss him. The principal did not yield to these demands, but suggested to the complaining parents that if they did not like the situation they could withdraw their children.

Harry Anderson and John Haire were only two of the many people who helped Williams when he lived in Edgerton. As a young man, Williams had decided that he wanted to be a physician, and he was fortunate that one of the more prominent physicians of the day, Henry Palmer, practiced in Janesville. During the Civil War, Dr. Palmer had been director of the largest Army hospital in the country and after the war was Surgeon General of Wisconsin. Palmer agreed to take Williams on as an apprentice. The year was 1878, and at the time apprenticing to a physician was still the most common way of going into medicine. During his apprenticeship Williams supported himself with barbering and stringing telephone lines.

At the end of two years of apprenticeship he could have set himself up in practice, but many new advances in medicine were taking place and Williams could take advantage of these new developments only in a medical school. Not the least of the new developments was the adoption of aseptic technique. That is, surgeons in the United States were finally taking the trouble to wash their hands and sterilize instruments before operations.

Aseptic technique had been pioneered by Joseph Lister

in England before the Civil War, and one of the greatest tragedies of that war was that aseptic technique had not yet caught on in the United States. Far more soldiers died from post-operative infections than directly from enemy bullets.

With the help of a one-hundred-dollar loan co-signed by Harry Anderson, Williams went to the Chicago Medical College, which later became the Medical School of Northwestern University. The course of instruction was eighteen months long, and at the time it was considered to be one of the most rigorous in the country. Anderson continued to help him with money, all of which Williams repaid. Williams graduated in 1883 and set up practice in Chicago.

When Williams started his practice the health situation for blacks was nothing less than desperate. The entire society was, of course, rigidly segregated, and this included hospitals and cemeteries. Most hospitals were reluctant to accept black patients, and when they did, even those who could afford to pay were put in charity wards where care was practically non-existent. Black doctors could not become affiliated with hospitals and, therefore, could not treat their own hospitalized patients.

Because of the difficulties of getting his patients into a hospital, Williams did a great deal of surgery in his offices and in his patient's homes. Williams proved to be a very skillful surgeon in conditions that were not exactly ideal. His skill as a physician and surgeon became known and he actually became affiliated with a hospital as a surgeon in Chicago's South Side Dispensary. Although it was not a full hospital (in the sense of medical services offered), Williams' appointment was quite remarkable at the time.

Since schools of nursing seldom admitted black women, black nurses were a rarity. Black women could, on occasion, get into schools of nursing if someone with influence intervened for them. Williams, as a well-known surgeon, did have such influence, and he did manage to get a few black women into nursing schools. It was the desperate shortage of black nurses and hospital facilities for blacks that prompted Williams to initiate the most ambitious project of his life. He determined to start a hospital that would be primarily for blacks, but not exclusively so. This hospital would also have a school of nursing.

Starting a hospital is a very complicated undertaking, requiring the cooperation of many people and liberal doses of money. Much of the support came from Chicago's black community. Williams' achievement was nothing less than fantastic. He conceived of the idea of the hospital in 1890, and a little more than a year later, in May of 1891, the Provident Hospital and Training School was a twelve-bed reality in a three-story building on Chicago's Twenty-ninth Street.

Williams set very rigid standards. In the first year he accepted only seven out of almost two hundred applicants for the nursing school. The staff included black and white physicians, and only men who had been to reputable medical schools were considered. In a few cases, however, Williams had to yield to pressures of important hospital trustees to appoint men whom he thought were not up to his standards. The hospital survived the depression of 1893, largely due to the efforts of Frederick Douglass, who came to Chicago and urged members of the black community to contribute.

The occasion for the heart operation came in 1893, when a young black teamster, James Cornish, was stabbed in a barroom brawl. The teamster received a one-inch wound in the chest. Although there was little external bleeding, the patient had gone into shock, which was indicative of severe blood loss from internal bleeding. Common medical procedure at the time for such cases was to give the patient a little morphine and keep him in bed. And the patient in shock usually died.

The only way Williams could see what was causing the trouble was to open the chest cavity and take a look. However, techniques of thoracic surgery were quite primitive and few patients survived such surgery. Williams was convinced that the young teamster would die if nothing was done. However, if he attempted contrived thoracic surgery and the patient still died, he could get himself into a great deal of trouble and possibly be permanently discredited. Williams could not just stand there and let the man die, so he decided on the surgery.

He asked six members of the staff to watch the procedure. With a scalpel he lengthened the stab wound into a six-inch incision. He then removed the fifth rib from its articulation with the sternum thereby exposing the heart. Williams found that a large blood vessel, the mammary artery, had been severed and that there was a laceration about 1¼ inches long in the pericardium, the membrane that covers the heart. The heart itself had a tiny nick in it which he decided to leave alone. (If the knife had entered a fraction of an inch to the right or left, one of the coronary arteries would have been cut and the patient would have been killed.)

But the cut pericardium needed attention. If left as it was, the cut ends could fuse to the pleura, a membrane between the lungs and chest wall, causing great pain. Williams decided to suture the pericardium, something that had never been done before. The suturing was done, the incision closed up, and the patient recovered completely.

A month after his release, however, Cornish was back in the hospital again with a head cut sustained in another barroom brawl. The wound was not serious, but Cornish would let no one but Williams sew up the cut. Williams did sew up Cornish again, but chewed him out royally and told him to get a job and send the hospital some money for its trouble. Cornish did get a job, and he sent ten dollars to the hospital. He lived until 1943.

The Freedman's Hospital in Washington, D.C., was the largest Negro hospital in the country in the 1890s. It was one of the hospitals set up by the Freedman's Bureau in the Reconstruction years as part of an effort to provide medical care for the newly freed slaves, and by the 1890s, it was the only one of these hospitals still in existence. In 1893 the position of chief surgeon at this hospital was open and Williams applied for the job. He was supported in his application by many prominent medical men. The position, however, was a political appointment and had opened up only because a Democrat, Grover Cleveland, had been re-elected President of the United States after a four-year absence. Despite a lot of political maneuvering for other less-qualified candidates, Williams got the job.

The hospital had deteriorated badly under previous chiefs, and the situation presented a great challenge to Williams. Williams completely reorganized the hospital, and brought it up to date with such measures as the inclusion of departments of bacteriology and pathology. He set up an internship program, which at the time was a rather new development in hospitals. He also started a school of nursing. And he applied the same rigid standards he had employed at Provident Hospital.

After the Republicans returned to power in 1896 political troubles began for Williams. His predecessor, Dr. Charles

Purvis, had never forgotten the sting of his removal in favor of Williams. And in his jealousy he made accusations against Williams that resulted in a Congressional investigation. No evidence was found to substantiate the charges of Purvis, but Williams had become thoroughly disgusted with Washington politics, and in 1898 he returned to Provident Hospital and the people there were glad to have their "Doctor Dan" back.

He became associated with other hospitals and with medical schools including Mercy Hospital, St. Luke's Hospital, and Meharry Medical College, a medical school for blacks in Nashville. He also worked with Booker T. Washington in an attempt to start a medical school at Tuskegee, which never became a reality.

The American Medical Association refused to admit black doctors, so Williams and others organized a black medical organization, The National Medical Association. An attempt to further reorganize Freedman's Hospital was effectively scuttled by Booker T. Washington, who had been successfully courted by some of the men Williams had rejected (because he felt that they were unqualified) at Provident and Freedman's. It would appear that Williams was a far better physician than he was a politician.

In 1912 Williams was offered the post of associate attending surgeon at Chicago's St. Luke's hospital. The appointment of a black physician to a very responsible position in a white hospital should have been an important milestone for Williams. But his enemies took advantage of it again to out-politic him. Williams was accused of being disloyal to his race, and when he was ordered to transfer his patients from St. Luke's to Provident, he refused and resigned from Provident. Even today it is an unfortunate aspect of medicine that directors of hospitals must frequently be as much politicians as they are doctors.

Williams remained at St. Luke's until his retirement. He received many honors, including charter membership in the American College of Surgeons founded in 1913. But for black physicians in general, Williams was an exception. The AMA continued to exclude black doctors, and black graduates of medical schools could not get internships in hospitals other than the few such as Freedman's and Provident. Williams had achieved much in a distinguished career, but when he died in 1931 the black physician still had a long way to go in achieving true professional freedom and recognition.

A COMMON BLOOD,

A COMMON BROTHERHOOD?

Charles Drew had more than his share of important decisions to make in his short life. He was an outstanding athlete and had to decide whether he would pursue the relatively open way for blacks in sports and become a professional athlete or take on the far more difficult task of becoming a black physician. Once he became a physician he had to decide whether to go into the affluence of private practice or the relative poverty and frustration of a black man in medical research. And an accident of genetics, which gave this man red hair and a light complexion, forced upon him what was perhaps the most momentous decision of all: was he to be black or attempt to "pass" into the white world?

Charles Drew was the oldest of the five children of Richard Drew, a carpet layer, and Nora Drew, a teacher. He was born in Washington, D.C. on June 3, 1904, and spent his childhood in the black slums of that city. At Dunbar High School in Washington he excelled scholastically, and in football, basketball, baseball and track he was equally proficient. The trophy cases were filled with the cups and statuettes won by Drew for his school, and he won various personal awards for being the most outstanding athlete at the school.

Drew attended Amherst College in Massachusetts on an athletic scholarship, and the years of his attendance are still remembered as the "golden years" of sports at Amherst. He lost out on a chance to go to the 1924 Olympics as a trackman by the toss of a coin. He and the man with whom he was competing for the spot on the team were so closely matched that the coach had to resort to the coin toss to make the decision. When Drew graduated in 1933 he was awarded a trophy for outstanding achievements in scholarship and athletics.

It was during the years at Amherst, when he was a campus hero, that he decided to be a doctor rather than a professional athlete. When he graduated he had no money for medical school, so he taught biology and chemistry for two years at Morgan College (now Morgan State College) in Baltimore, Maryland. He was also the athletic coach, and the tradition of this school as a producer of fine athletes dates from Drew's tenure here. Many of the most outstanding of today's professional football players are Morgan State graduates.

His first attempt to get into a medical school was a crushing disappointment. In 1928 he applied to Howard, a black medical school. He was rejected as a medical student but was offered a job as athletic coach! This rejection seemed to be the end of Drew's hopes for a medical career. But starting on the day he received the rejection from Howard, he wrote letters of application to scores of medical schools in the United States and Canada. And a positive response came from McGill University in Montreal.

At the time, athletic programs were maintained in many

medical schools, and after Drew's arrival the trophy cases at McGill were filled with new cups and statuettes as they had been at Dunbar High and Amherst. The world-wide depression that followed the stock market collapse of 1929 upset Drew's plans to get through school with part-time and summer jobs. There were just no jobs at all, and the income he obtained from refereeing and umpiring was not enough. He was saved from the necessity of dropping out by a fellowship from The Rosenwald Fund.

At McGill, he was a student of Dr. John Beattie, an Englishman who had done research in blood chemistry. Dr. Beattie's influence had much to do with Drew's decision to go into research and teaching rather than private practice. Drew also came to the attention of many prominent white physicians, not a few of whom urged him to "pass" for white and enter their world.

Drew rejected both the prospect of conveniently becoming white and the material rewards of private practice. Drew graduated from McGill in 1932, second in his class, and with membership in Alpha Omega Alpha, an honorary scholastic fraternity for medical students.

In Canada, Drew did not have the difficulties experienced by American black medical school graduates in getting an internship. He was placed in Montreal General, the hospital considered most desirable by Canadian medical school graduates.

At Montreal General, Drew found some time to devote to blood research. At the time, blood-tranfusion techniques had come a long way since Karl Landsteiner discovered the four basic blood groups in 1900. Before that time transfusions were attempted only when there was nothing else left to do. Sometimes patients would make remarkable recoveries following transfusions. But on other occasions the

Charles Drew. (*Courtesy of Howard University*)

patient would die in agony. The reasons for this rather sharp disparity in the effects of blood transfusions were unknown, and physicians were reluctant to play this game of medical Russian Roulette.

In 1900 Landsteiner found that the problem was in the specific nature of certain proteins found in erythrocytes—red blood cells—and the plasma—liquid part of the blood. Landsteiner found two basic types of proteins in the red cells, which he designated as A and B. An individual could have one, both, or none of these proteins in his blood cells. The blood types A, B, and AB are based on the possession of these proteins. O designates the lack of possession of these proteins. If A blood, for example, was transfused into a person with B blood, proteins in the plasma of the receiver would react with the proteins in the blood cells of the donor and cause the blood cells to come together into clumps of cells. These clumps could block smaller blood vessels, and if the vessels were in vital organs, unpleasant complications or even death might be the result.

As the result of Landsteiner's work, it became possible to match the blood of prospective donors against that of the recipient. By the 1930s transfusions were no longer flirtations with death, but they still provided moments of drama that must have been an inspiration for the writers of radio soap operas. When a patient was in need of a transfusion, anxious relatives were summoned to the hospital where they solemnly assembled to have their blood matched against that of the patient. Every transfusion was a race against time. And the scene must indeed have been dramatic, if one relative after the next proved to have the wrong type. Sometimes the race was lost. The individual who happened not to have any relatives or who was in an accident away from home was in a tenuous situation if he needed blood.

Drew was intrigued with the possibility of storing blood in "banks" and thereby ending the frantic drama that always accompanied transfusions. There were, of course, many problems to overcome before blood banks could become a reality. Blood, as any other product of living things, will decompose if removed from the organism of which it was a part. The red cells start to deteriorate very quickly, and the blood tends to clot. Refrigeration had been tried, but at best, the usefulness of the blood was extended by only a matter of hours. Freezing with methods available in the 1930s resulted in destruction of the red cells. Drew was familiar with a technique developed in Russia that involved mixing the blood with a little sodium citrate. The citrated blood could be stored for several days and still be used. The technique had drawbacks, such as some loss of the ability of the blood to fight off infection. And there were many other unanswered questions about citrated blood. But before Drew could start to look for answers, he had another job to do at Howard University, which was in deep trouble and needed the magic of Charles Drew.

Drew went on to a year's residency at Montreal General and in 1935 was named Diplomate of the National Board of Examiners, which meant that he was now a certified specialist in surgery. He became an instructor of pathology at Howard and at Freedman's Hospital which had become associated with Howard. There was an air of despondency at Howard, brought on by the knowledge of the students that as black men they would never be fully admitted into the medical fraternity. Drew breathed new life into the school with a zeal that was part football coach, part demanding academian, and a little bit of missionary. He demanded nothing less than excellence and his students responded. They started to call him the "Great White Father."

The Rockefeller Foundation, in 1938, informed Howard that it would grant a two-year fellowship at Columbia University to one of the Howard instructors. Drew was chosen, and he went to work with Dr. John Scudder, who had done a great deal of research in blood chemistry. In addition to his research, he worked a full round of duty at Columbia's Presbyterian Hospital as a resident in surgery.

Drew's primary interest was finding a way to extend the time blood could be stored and still be usable. This was the key to maintaining a blood bank. Drew experimented with different amounts of sodium citrate and kept the citrated blood at 4° C., just a little above freezing. He was able to extend the storage limit to about a week. Additionally, he found that extremely careful handling of the blood was important. Rough handling tended to hasten the breakdown of the red cells, and once the red cells had disintegrated the blood was useless for transfusions. Drew was given a small grant by Landsteiner's Blood Betterment Association for his blood-bank work.

Drew had taken on an almost impossible schedule. He continued to put in a full tour at Presbyterian Hospital, and he was writing his thesis titled "Banked Blood," which was based on the research he was doing. He did, however, manage to find time to go to a conference at Tuskegee to deliver a report on his work in transfusions. And during a stopover in Atlanta he met Lenore Robbins, who was a teacher at Spellman College. On the way back from Tuskegee, he stopped off in Atlanta again and asked Miss Robbins to be his wife. The startled Miss Robbins accepted and some six months later, in September of 1939, Drew managed to get a weekend off so that he could be married.

The same month that Drew and Lenore Robbins were married, Hitler sent his armies into Poland and the Second World War was under way. In the course of his research Drew had proposed the possibility of storing plasma rather than whole blood in blood banks. Plasma had many advantages over whole blood. It had everything that whole blood had, except the red cells, which were the cause of all the trouble when attempts were made to store blood. Since there were no blood cells to break down, plasma could be stored indefinitely. No red cells meant that anyone, regardless of blood type, could receive plasma from any donor. This was particularly important on battlefields and in bombed cities where there was no time to match blood. For battlefield injuries, plasma was just as effective as whole blood in restoring fluid to the body, thereby reversing shock. The wounded could be kept alive until they were brought to a hospital where they could receive whole blood if it was needed. Since plasma could be stored for long periods of time, it could readily be transported to battlefields.

Drew obtained a grant to carry out more research in plasma, and the results he obtained in experiments were gratifying. Plasma proved to be very effective in the treatment of burn victims and in excessive blood loss. Drew was sure enough of his work to propose the use of plasma in massive wartime programs. He made such a proposal to the National Blood Transfusion Committee, which met to consider the blood needs of France. Drew convinced the committee of the advantages of plasma and was named to direct the Plasma for France program. However, before the program could get started, the French armies collapsed and France was forced to capitulate.

In June of 1940 Drew was awarded the degree of Doctor of Science in medicine. He was the first American black man to earn this degree. Drew returned to Howard as head of the department of surgery. The war in Europe went on, and a plasma program for Britain had been initiated. The British plasma program was chaotic. Much of the plasma shipped from the United States arrived spoiled. There was no standardization of technique among the various hospitals that supplied plasma. John Beattie, Drew's professor at McGill, was head of the British Transfusion Service, and when confronted with the mess he knew there was but one person in the United States who could straighten it out. Drew accepted the offer and went to New York to take over the program. He centralized the direction of the various blood-collecting centers, such as hospitals, and achieved a uniform high standard of operation. Drew continued as head of the Plasma for Britain project until early 1941, when the British were able to start their own program based on Drew's organizational methods.

Hardly had Drew finished the Plasma for Britain project, when he was asked to take on another job. By 1941 it was generally conceded that the United States was going to get into the war. The only question was when. In preparation for war, a National Blood Bank program was organized by the National Research Council. The Red Cross was named as the administrating agency. Drew was the logical choice to be medical director of this program and again he accepted.

In addition to directing the preparation of thousands of gallons of liquid plasma, Drew initiated research on methods of preparing frozen and dried plasma.

Drew's concentration on the task at hand was shattered when he learned that the military had specified that only blood from Caucasians was acceptable. If blood from blacks was to be accepted at all, it was to be segregated and used only for transfusion to blacks. Drew was faced with a dilemma. He knew that his work was important and he wanted to continue. But he could not tolerate the white-only policy, which was based on superstition and ignorance and had absolutely no scientific justification. The military and the Red Cross had yielded to the completely fallacious belief that hereditary factors were carried in blood, and that if a white received blood from a black donor he would turn black, or his offspring would be black. Red Cross officials and the more enlightened military people were certainly aware of the stupidity of the all-white policy, and this knowledge made their acquiescence even more inexcusable. The Red Cross offered the excuse that the all-white policy was necessary if the cooperation of large segments of the population was to be obtained.

Drew protested the policy of ignorance, but it was continued. So he felt that he had no choice but to resign. He called a press conference to announce his reasons for resigning. Among his remarks at the press conference were:

> . . . The disservice that has been done, has been done not only to the Negro people but to the cause of truth itself. How have we, in this age and in this hour, allowed once again to creep into our hearts the dark myths and wretched superstitions of the past . . . In the laboratory I have found that you and I share a common blood; but will we ever, ever share a common brotherhood? As repugnant as this scientific fact may appear to some, their quarrel is not with me, but with the Giver of Life whose wisdom made it so.

Drew returned to Howard where he was made full professor. Under his leadership the surgery department attained a new level of excellence. Under Drew's tutelage, two students from Howard Medical took the examinations for admission to the American Board of Surgery. Not only did they pass (and thus became the first Howard graduates to qualify for the Board), but they ranked first and second respectively. Other successful candidates followed and Drew urged them to seek internships and residencies in hospitals run by the white medical establishment rather than remain at Howard as had been the pattern in the past. Black graduates of medical schools began to experience less difficulty in obtaining internships, and this change in attitude was due in no small measure to the success of Drew's students.

In 1944, the same year he was appointed chief of staff at Freedman's Hospital Drew was awarded the Spingarn Medal. And in 1947 he traveled to Amherst College to receive an honorary Doctor of Science degree.

In 1949 he was named surgical consultant to the Armed Forces. By this time the military no longer insisted that its white soldiers receive only blood from white donors. As part of this job he traveled throughout Europe investigating the standards of military medical installations.

By 1950 he had been a physician for over fifteen years. But contrary to the statistics showing that physicians have higher incomes than other occupational groups, Drew's average annual income was less than that of most factory workers. He had chosen to be a black medical researcher rather than a white private practitioner, and he knew that this decision meant he would never make much money. His many blood research projects and his duties at Howard kept him from even maintaining a part-time practice that would have brought in additional income.

Almost every year Drew attended a medical conference at Tuskegee. He had been on his way to this same conference in 1939 when he had met his wife. For the 1950 conference, he felt that his round of activities at the hospital had fatigued him too much to drive, and so he decided to go by train. At the last minute he changed his mind, so that he could drive three of the doctors from Freedman's who could not afford the train fare.

By dawn of April 1, 1950, the quartet of doctors in Drew's automobile was nearing Burlington, North Carolina. Drew was taking his turn at the wheel while the others attempted to sleep. Tired from a full schedule of surgery the day before, he fell asleep at the wheel. In the accident that followed, the three other doctors received only bruises, but Drew was partially thrown out of the car, and the vehicle rolled over him.

Drew was still alive, but bleeding from internal and external wounds, when the ambulance arrived at the hospital. He was given plasma, but it was too late and he died.

Drew was eulogized in an editorial in the Washington *Post:*

> . . . He chose to devote his gifts to the advancement of medicine rather than to the advancement of a personal career or to winning the monetary rewards that were easily within his reach . . . It is said that more than half of the Negro surgeons who have been certified by the American Board of Surgery were trained by Dr. Drew himself, the first Negro to serve as an examiner on the board . . . He will be missed, however, not alone by his own race, but by his whole profession and by men everywhere who value scientific devotion and integrity.

Opening the Hallowed Halls

Scientists claim to be just like anybody else, and in many respects they are. But there are many things that make scientists special. They must have much more education than almost any other occupational group. Their activities are mostly unknown to the general public. Of course, some, such as Einstein, have become household words. But for every Einstein, Watson, or Urey there are thousands of scientists completely unknown to the general public who devote their lives to work that is significant to all mankind.

The nature of scientific work has resulted in the evolution of the "community" of scientists. Each "community" is made up of scientists within a particular field, such as physics, chemistry, and biology, and within the various branches of these major sciences smaller "communities" exist. There are no official rules for admission to the scientific community, but admission is difficult, and it is even more difficult to maintain one's position within the community. From six to eight years of college and graduate study are usually required to earn the Ph.D. degree, which is the essential "ticket of admission." Courses of study in science are very exacting and difficult; they demand all of the student's time and attention. A student whose economic situation requires that he "work his way through" will be hard-pressed to keep up with his studies and to compete with his fellow students. If the student has also been denied a solid basic primary and secondary education, he will find his situation nearly hopeless. Small wonder that the ranks of the scientific community have been notably lacking in people who are members of groups that can be described as "disadvantaged."

The incompatability of "disadvantage" and science can be shown by comparing the situations that existed in pre-World War I Germany and Russia. In Czarist Russia, Jews were particularly oppressed. They were permitted to reside only in certain parts of the country, and they were kept out of many lines of work. It was almost impossible for a Jewish child to obtain education beyond primary school, and therefore there were very few, if any, Jewish scientists in Czarist Russia. At the same time, in Imperial Germany, while there was some social discrimination against Jews, members of this group were not denied the opportunity to obtain an education. And the number of German Jews in science far exceeded their percentage of the total German population.

Parallels can be drawn between the Jews of Czarist Russia and blacks in the United States. The oppression that was slavery is obvious, and it is also well known that the op-pression of blacks continued (and continues) after the Emancipation. The states of the former Confederacy were slow to establish public schools for blacks, and even when they did the "separate but equal" facilities that were set up hardly commanded the descriptive term of school. The *situation was little better in the northern states. Where legal segregation did not exist, patterns of residential segregation dictated segregated schools. And such schools, usually in the run-down parts of cities, almost always received the short end of whatever money was available for education. The result was that blacks, already at a disadvantage because of color prejudice, were forced to compete in a fast-moving society with an inadequate education. It was a very difficult situation for a black man who wanted to be a scientist.*

There were many well-meaning attempts to correct the black's educational situation. These ranged from the often pitiful Freedmen's Schools of the Reconstruction Era to huge philanthropies such as The Rosenwald Fund. This fund was endowed by a philanthropist, Julius Rosenwald, to provide financial aid for individuals or groups who, in the judgment of the trustees of the fund, "helped advance the Negroes." However, efforts such as The Rosenwald Fund have been criticized for actually fostering segregation in their bequests for hospitals and colleges designated for blacks only. The black colleges that were set up in the South only partially filled the need, and they had many problems, not the least of which was obtaining faculty from a group of people who were already educationally deprived. These colleges, for all their shortcomings in their early days, fulfilled an important need. They were houses of learning when most others were closed to blacks. And they provided a platform from which a few blacks managed to battle their way into the scientific community and open the way for many others.

The number of black scientists in America is rapidly increasing, and it is not possible here to tell the stories of all the black men and women who have distinguished themselves in scientific work. Scientists are supposed to possess the quality of the open mind. But, unfortunately, many of them were blighted with unscientific racial prejudices, and these attitudes made it even more difficult for the trail blazers whose stories follow.

As far as is known, the first black man to receive a doctorate in a science was Edward Bouchet, who took a Ph.D. in physics from Yale University in 1876 and was elected to Phi Beta Kappa in the process. The topic of his doctoral dissertation was "Measuring Refractive Indices." He went on to a teaching career.

Finding a job was a serious problem for many blacks who obtained advanced degrees in science. Charles Henry Turner received his doctorate from the University of Chicago in 1907. His field was animal behavior with a specialization in insect behavior. At the time, animal behavior was not the active science it is today. There were few jobs for specialists in animal behavior, and Turner found that the few that were around were not for a black man. Turner taught at a high school in St. Louis. He did not allow his lack of teaching affiliation with a university to keep him from being active in his chosen field. He continued to write papers, some fifty of which were published in scientific journals, until his death in 1923.

Turner's situation was repeated throughout the South. In the era of segregated schools there were about twice as many black teachers with Ph.D.s (mostly in education) in southern public schools as there were white public school teachers with the same degrees. This was due to the fact that most blacks with doctorates could not find jobs in colleges and industry.

WASTED IN THE LAND OF HIS BIRTH

One of the first black men to gain some acceptance into the scientific community was Ernest Everett Just, who made many significant contributions as a cell biologist. His battle for a basic education, admission to a college, and struggle for recognition are typical of the difficulties many black scientists faced.

Just was born in Charleston, South Carolina, in 1884. His father, who worked on the Charleston waterfront, died when Ernest was four. His mother had received training as a teacher and was able to support herself and her boy. She was very ambitious for her son, and it was through his mother that he developed a love for learning. Mrs. Just was an idealist, and she attempted to organize a model community among the black workers in the phosphate fields outside of Charleston. The attempt was unsuccessful. She tried to build a school and was cheated by building-supplies dealers. Soon after the school was finally built it burned down, and the model community disintegrated.

Ernest's mother had been driven to build the school by her firsthand knowledge of the completely rotten excuses for schools provided for black children in the South. Ernest attended something called the Industrial School of Orangeburg, which was supposed to be a public school for black children. Both Ernest and his mother were convinced that he had gained nothing from the Orangeburg school other than learning how to read. They felt that if Ernest wanted to get a real education he would have to go North. So in 1900, at the age of seventeen, he worked his way to New York on a steamship. When he arrived in New York his total resources were five dollars and two pairs of shoes. Just considered the second pair of shoes to be far more prestigious than the five dollars.

In New York, from a newspaper, the *Christian Endeavor World*, he learned of a school in Meriden, New Hampshire, The Kimball School, which, as a policy, accepted black boys on a tuition-free basis. In less than four weeks he had erned enough money to travel to New Hampshire and to enroll in the school.

Although Ernest had been to school in South Carolina, it was felt that because of the poor quality of his education he had better start at the lowest class. Ernest did very well at Kimball and completed four years of work in three. He was editor of the school newspaper and president of the debating society.

With the aid of loans and scholarships, he went to Dartmouth College. Just had developed into a serious, scholarly young man, and he was annoyed and disappointed when he found that the undergraduate student body seemed more concerned with football and the Winter Festival than with academic pursuits. In short, Dartmouth bored him. He thought at first he might want to major in Greek and concentrate on the philosopher and statesman, Demosthenes. But he gave up this idea when he found that a great deal of research had already been done on Demosthenes and there would be, he felt, little challenge in this study.

Just plodded through his freshman year with a mediocre record. Midway through his sophomore year he had decided to quit Dartmouth. But then he enrolled in his first biology class and he was completely fascinated. He was particularly inspired by a teacher, the zoologist William Patten, and from that point on, Just knew he had to be a biologist. The transformation was miraculous. He graduated in 1907, *magna cum laude,* a member of Phi Beta Kappa, and with special honors in zoology and history (even though his official major was English).

He went directly from Dartmouth to a teaching job at Howard University. In 1912 he spent his first summer at the Marine Biological Laboratories at Woods Hole, Massachusetts. Woods Hole was, and still is, a mecca for all kinds of biologists, especially marine biologists. Some of the most significant work in the fields of marine biology, embryology, and cell physiology have been carried out in this legendary laboratory on the shores of Nantucket Sound.

During the first two years at Woods Hole he was a research assistant to Dr. Frank R. Lillie, head of the Zoology Department at the University of Chicago. At Woods Hole, Lillie and Just worked on fertilization, utilizing the eggs of Nereis (sandworms) and sea urchins. The sea urchin is related to the starfish, and its eggs are particularly suitable for research. The sea urchin was so widely used at Woods Hole that the creature became a legend in itself.

Dr. Lillie was so impressed with Just that he invited him to work under him in a doctoral program. Just earned his Ph.D. in 1916 from the University of Chicago, with financial help from the National Research Council. He would have obtained the degree a couple of years earlier, but the pressure of his work at Howard kept him from devoting full time to his doctoral work. At Howard, he worked on problems of medical education and spent some time on the same problem at other black institutions, in an advisory capacity. In 1915 his work came to the attention of the NAACP, which had just instituted the Spingarn Medal and they decided to award it to Just. His reply to the Secretary of the NAACP upon receiving notification of the award, was one that could be expected of a scientist:

> . . . It rather upsets me to learn that I am expected to be present at the Award, doubtless in the presence of a large audience. I feel deeply that I ought not to court publicity since such courtship ought to be incompatible with scientific endeavor.

Reluctantly, Just attended the presentation ceremony and was thoroughly embarrassed at being the center of attention of so many people.

After obtaining his doctorate, he returned to Howard where he remained for almost all his professional career. He was revered by generations of Howard students and inspired many of his students to pursue science careers. However, Howard was a relatively young school and did not have the research facilities that were characteristic of older, more venerable institutions. His teaching load was heavy, and he would have had little time for research even if the facilities were there. His life was characterized by a conflict between his desire to engage in basic research and his obligation to his students. It was a conflict that has torn many devoted teachers.

Just was removed from the mainstream of biological research at Howard, but he returned to that mainstream every summer at Woods Hole. There he carried out research on a number of problems including the relationship of the point of entrance of the sperm cell to the development pattern of Nereis eggs, artificial parthenogenesis (development of an embryo without fertilization), the nature of the cell membrane, and various problems in cell genetics. He contributed many papers to scientific journals and would have written more had his research not been limited to summers. At Woods Hole, he became an associate editor of the journals, *Biological Bulletin, Physiological Zoology,* and the *Journal of Morphology.* He was also a contributing editor to *General Zoology.*

The color of Just's skin should not have been any problem in the world of the scientist. But Just was never fully accepted in the community of biologists, even though his investigations were entirely credible and he never violated any of the unwritten rules of the scientific community —such as making unfounded claims or seeking publicity. It is common practice for active scientists to be invited as guest lecturers on campuses other than their own. But Just seldom, if ever, received such invitations from white universities. Scientists, like anyone else, can be afflicted with racial prejudice.

Just's chances of penetrating further into the scientific community were hurt by his stand on the role of the cell nucleus in the activities of the cell. Genetics was a new and very active science in the 1920s and 1930s at the peak of Just's career. A massive collection of evidence pointing to the nucleus as the center of the cell's activity was being gathered at laboratories all over the world. Work done by Thomas Hunt Morgan and others at Columbia University with the fruit fly, *Drosophila,* had almost conclusively shown that the genes, which were considered to be the hereditary factors, were located on the chromosomes. And chromosomes were found only in the cell nucleus.

Just could not go along with the all-powerful role assigned to the nucleus. And in taking this stand he was in direct opposition to the great majority of biological opinion. It was a brave stand for Just, who was already at enough of a disadvantage. Just held that the cytoplasm (the rest of the cell outside the nucleus) was just as important, if not more important than the nucleus in directing the cell's activity. Just pointed out that all of the different cells in the bodies of living things, such as bone cells, muscle cells, nerve cells, etc., had the same chromosomes and, therefore, presumably the same genes, and yet the various cells were different. This is indeed one of the weakest points in the entire gene theory of inheritance; how can genes be the determining factors if the same genes exist in very different kinds of cells in the same organism?

Recent work in elucidating the nature of the gene, such as the Watson-Crick DNA model, the cracking of the genetic code, and the isolation of specific units of DNA that have been shown to be individual genes, has tended to show that Just's extreme view on the dominance of cytoplasm over the nucleus was not entirely correct. However, this recent work has also shown that the geneticists and cytologists of the 1920s and 1930s who gave exclusive dominance to the nucleus were not entirely correct either. It has been shown that the synthesis of protein, which is the key to all life activity, takes place on ribosomes, which are in the cytoplasm. Cytoplasmic DNA (genes) has been found, and there is strong evidence that the total activity of the cell is the result of an interplay and feedback of chemical information between the cytoplasm and the nucleus. This feedback of information between cytoplasm and nucleus apparently turns genes "off" and "on" and may be the explanation of why cells with the same genes can be as different as are skin and nerve cells, for example. Certain cytoplasmic influences on cell heredity and, therefore, the heredity of the entire organism were demonstrated in Just's lifetime. As is frequently the case in scientific controversies, all parties in the dispute were both a little right and a little wrong.

Just's opinions on cytoplasm were a scientist's efforts to arrive at a scientific truth. It is unfortunate that men such as Just, who hold opinions contrary to the popular tide of the moment, are frequently ostracized within the scientific community. This is contrary to the "open mind" that is supposed to be a salient characteristic of the scientist. Just's views on the role of cytoplasm were somewhat prophetic of developments that were to occur after his death. He made statements that genes functioned "in cell heredity only in as much as they take substances from the cytoplasm. . . ." The recent cracking of the genetic code has demonstrated that DNA directs the assembly of amino acids, which are *in the cytoplasm,* into protein. And most of the proteins so assembled are enzymes, which are the direct determinants of cell activity.

Just's work on the cell membrane was also prophetic of future developments. During Just's lifetime most biologists believed that the cell membrane was only a "semi-permeable" covering that merely covered the cell and allowed certain substances to enter and leave the cell through the passive mechanism of osmosis. Just held that the cell membrane was an active component of the cell and more than just a covering. Work with the electron microscope, which was not generally available in Just's lifetime, has upheld many of his views on the cells membrane.

Just left Howard University only on the occasions he was

invited to work at various European laboratories, including the Kaiser Wilhelm Institute in Germany, the Sorbonne in Paris, and the Naples Zoological Laboratory. He also did some work in Russian laboratories and was invited to stay there permanently. Working in these laboratories was a great honor accorded to very few scientists. The invitations he received from the European laboratories were an indictment of American institutions, which lacked the courage to depart from established patterns of segregation and invite a black man into their laboratories and lecture halls.

In 1939, only two years before his death, Just published two books, *Basic Methods for Experiments in Eggs of Marine Animals,* and *The Biology of the Cell Surface.* The first book was for many years a valuable source of information for biologists who worked with sea urchin eggs and the eggs of other marine invertebrates. In the latter book, he discussed his ideas of the active role of the cell membrane and his hypotheses of cytoplasmic inheritance.

Just's exclusion from American biological institutions was decried by many concerned American scientists. The death of the eminent physiologist, Jacques Loeb, vacated a position at the Rockefeller Institute, where Loeb had been working on parthenogenesis. Just, who had done extensive work on this subject, was a logical candidate for the job, but the Rockefeller Institute made no offer. The Dean of the University of Minnesota Medical School severely lashed the Rockefeller Foundation for its hypocrisy, and in this particular instance, for its lack of courage in refusing to shatter the precedents of racial segregation.

When Ernest Just died in 1941, his old friend and teacher, Frank Lillie, said in eulogy:

His death was premature and his work unfinished; but his accomplishments were many and worthy of remembrance. That a man of his ability, scientific devotion and of such strong personal loyalties as he gave and received should have been wasted in the land of his birth must remain a matter for regret.

ELIGIBLE FOR THE KINGDOM OF THE GODS

Some scientists, such as Ernest Just, devote their lives to basic research, a search for knowledge for its own sake with little thought to its practical applications. Others, such as Percy Lavon Julian, carry out research that though basic, can be of immediate benefit to mankind. Both kinds of scientists are important. The basic researcher adds to the fund of man's knowledge, and the knowledge he discovers may indeed provide the applied researcher with the basic information to make discoveries that can improve the quality of life.

Even when he was a child, there seemed little doubt that Percy Julian would go on to great things. He was one of six children in a family in which the pursuit of learning was a way of life. All of the six children in this Alabama family obtained college degrees; two of them became physicians. The tradition of learning had started early in the Julian family. When Percy's grandfather was a slave, his master had had two of this man's fingers cut off his hand as a punishment for learning to read and write.

Percy attended segregated schools in Montgomery, Alabama. When he was of high school age, the state of Alabama maintained only one high school in Birmingham as its "separate but equal" offering to all black children in Alabama. The "school" in Birmingham was so bad as to be out of the question, so Percy went to the state Normal School for Negroes in Montgomery, an institution that had been started by a Scotsman in the Reconstruction Era with the aid of white teachers from the North. The school suffered from the capricious "benevolence" of the Alabama white establishment. The Alabama Legislature at one point appropriated funds for it and later, in 1915, passed a law that forbade white teachers to teach in black schools. This was at a time when the denial of educational opportunities to Negroes resulted in the preparation of very few qualified black teachers.

Julian was accepted at Indiana's De Pauw University in 1916. It hardly bears repeating that as a Negro from the South, his basic education was not worth the time he had spent acquiring it. Julian was the product of a segregated system that seemed dedicated to the frequently repeated southern bromide that "All a black needs to learn is how to say yes sir, no sir, to a white man, and gee and haw to a mule."

Julian was admitted to De Pauw on probation and as such was not even a full freshman. At that, his situation was a marked improvement over that of George Washington Carver who had been thirty years old before he gained admission to a college. But Julian was also to experience frustrating delays brought about solely because of his color. His freshman and sophomore years were very busy. In addition to regular college courses, he had to take "make-up" high school courses. He also held down a job as a waiter in a white fraternity house. Julian, majoring in chemistry, grad-

uated in 1920 at the top of his class, valedictorian, and
with membership in Phi Beta Kappa and Sigma Xi; it was
a remarkable record for a man who only supposed to know
"yes, sir; no, sir; gee, and haw."

Julian's troubles were only beginning. Graduate school on
a fellowship was the next step. But despite his brilliant
academic record, he was unable to find a graduate school
that would have him. His adviser, Professor Blanchard,
wrote to a number of graduate schools on Julian's behalf,
but they all refused the application, offering such excuses
as that Julian would be unable to get a job upon graduation
either in industry or in a white university.

Julian took the advice of his professor and found a
teaching job at Fisk University, a black college in Nashville,
Tennessee. He remained at Fisk for two years until he had
an opportunity to compete for a fellowship in chemistry at
Harvard University. The Austin Fellowship was awarded on
a competitive basis, and when Julian won it no one could
deny him the opportunity. But he had lost two years.

Julian's achievement at Harvard was outstanding. He
earned the highest grades in his group and received his
Master's degree in 1923. But it was still not enough. Julian
was not given the usual teaching assistantship that came
with a brilliant academic performance. The men who
awarded assistantships were afraid that "someone's" sen-
sibilities might be offended by a black teacher. (The "someone" might only be an undergraduate from Georgia, but
the undergraduate's father might be a rich alumnus who
distributed largess at the annual alumni giving.)

In trying to get into a doctoral program, Julian had the
same difficulties he had experienced in his attempts at a
Master's program. So he again took a job in a black college,
this time in West Virginia, and later at Howard University,

where he served on the same faculty with Ernest Just. Not until 1929 was he able to start his doctoral studies, in Vienna under the well-known organic chemist, Ernest Späth, on a fellowship from the General Education Board. He obtained his Ph.D. degree in 1931 and returned to Howard where he was made head of the chemistry department. While he was at Vienna he developed an interest in the potentialities of the soybean as a source of useful products. The soybean had been a food staple in China for centuries before Western chemists discovered it and began to synthesize a myriad of materials from its substance. And this bean was later to be the focal point of Julian's most significant work.

When Julian returned to Howard, he directed his attention to a drug called physostigmine. This substance was used to treat the eye disease glaucoma. The usual source of the drug was the plant *Physostigma,* commonly known as the Calabar bean. Julian wanted to analyze the structure of the physostigmine molecule and determine a method of synthesizing it. The artificial synthesis of substances found in nature has long been a preoccupation of organic chemists. The synthesized substance can usually be made in greater quantities and therefore more cheaply than the same substance extracted from its natural source.

Julian invited two of his Vienna colleagues to join him in his physostigmine work. Julian and his co-workers had hardly started when the Howard University administration expressed displeasure at his apparent preference for research rather than for teaching. Julian felt it advisable to leave Howard, and his friend, Dr. Blanchard, who had heard of his work, invited him to continue it at De Pauw. Julian was appointed instructor of organic chemistry and the university officials were cooperative in arranging a teaching schedule that would allow him time for his research. Julian had come to De Pauw on such short notice that no money had been appropriated to outfit a laboratory. With the help of Dr. Blanchard, money was begged from a variety of sources including interested alumni and even some university officials.

After two years of work Julian's research team had produced molecules that he believed to be the precursors of physostigmine. If what he had were indeed the precursors, then he was only a few steps away from the actual synthesis of physostigmine. In 1934 he published papers on his precursors in the *Journal of the American Chemical Society*, and his work was widely discussed among chemists. When he was very close to success, two setbacks occurred in rapid succession. The first problem was that De Pauw could no longer support his work. This problem was solved when the Rosenwald Fund made grants sufficient to support Julian for another two years.

The second setback was not so easily solved. Dr. Robert Robinson of Oxford University in England published papers in which he claimed to have attained precursors to physostigmine by a process completely different from Julian's. Julian had struggled to overcome racial prejudice and get as far as he had in his career. A scientific controversy in which he could very well be discredited might, at this point, be permanently damaging to his hopes for a career as a chemist. Other scientists had lost out in controversies and had gone on to other work without losing the respect of their colleagues. But a black scientist trying to prove himself at an early point in his career might not get a second chance.

Julian had confidence in the quality of his work, and he decided to challenge Robinson. He claimed that his method was the better one and that he would arrive at synthetic physostigmine before Robinson did. And in February of 1935 he and his Vienna colleague, Dr. Pikl, did just that. The proof came from a comparison of the melting points of natural physostigmine and what Julian claimed to be the synthetic product. The melting point of Julian's synthetic substance was determined to be exactly the same as that of natural physostigmine and the proof was conclusive; Julian had synthesized physostigmine.

Julian was widely acclaimed in the community of chemists and Blanchard wanted to make him head of De Pauw's chemistry department. The appointment, however, was vetoed by other people connected with the university. It appeared that Julian would never get anywhere in the academic world no matter how brilliant his achievements. Frightened little men on boards of trustees would always block his way, not daring to run the risk of "offending."

Julian wanted to be a research chemist. The situation at black colleges demanded full-time teachers rather than research men. The white academic world had provided nothing but frustration. So Julian turned to industry. In industry, once a man had proved he could produce profit-making products for the company, the only color that mattered was the color of the ink in the ledger books. This is not to say that all industries opened their doors for blacks. Julian was exceptional in many ways. But his first job offer was a disappointment. There was a position available at the Institute of Paper Chemistry in Appleton, Wisconsin, which later proved to be totally unfeasible for Julian to accept: it was revealed that Appleton had a law (surely unconstitutional) that forbade the "housing of a Negro overnight."

Julian was offered the job of chief chemist and director of research at the Glidden Company, a paint manufacturer.

There he was able to return to the soybean work that had fascinated him when he was a graduate student at Vienna. The proteins he isolated from soybeans were used in the manufacture of paper coatings, fabric sizings, water-base paints, and to formulate a foam that was dramatically effective in extinguishing oil and gasoline fires. The directors of the Glidden Company knew what they were doing when they hired Julian. In the first year of Julian's employ, the company advanced from a thirty-thousand-dollar loss to a pre-tax profit of $135,000.

The Glidden Company did not insist that Julian limit his research to paint and related products. Julian enjoyed as much, if not more, freedom in his choice of research projects as he would have had in a university laboratory. Most importantly, he did not have to worry about running out of money before a project was completed. The constant scramble for grants and fellowships was a thing of the past.

Julian's interest in soybean chemistry continued, and he commenced a project on synthesizing hormones from the versatile little bean. Hormones are substances that regulate life processes in living things, including people. A variety of diseases are caused by a deficiency or an overabundance of hormones. Such diseases are frequently treated with hormones extracted from animals that have been killed in slaughter houses. But this treatment is usually at great expense. One injection of a pituitary gland hormone, for example, might represent the pituitary glands of a thousand slaughtered animals. So, inexpensive processes for synthesizing hormones from soybeans or other cheap sources were very much needed.

The first hormone project was the synthesis of progesterone and testosterone, the male and female sex hormones. These hormones belong to a class of chemicals called steroids; animal fats are also steroids and steroid substances tend to form insoluble masses when they are extracted by chemical means. The insolubility of this steroid mass, which is somewhat like grease, can make further chemical manipulation slow and difficult and, therefore, expensive. Julian solved the problem of the soybean steroids by the addition of quicklime, which literally filled the mass full of holes so that various solvents could get at the substance from all directions. This was the key step that made possible the synthesis of large amounts of progesterone and testosterone from soybeans. The price of the hormones was sharply reduced, and people who needed them for therapy no longer had to risk bankruptcy to get them.

Arthritis is an old affliction of man. Some of the fossil bones of Neanderthal and Cro Magnon men show the effects of this disease. For centuries sufferers from arthritis have been willing to pay anything for relief from the terrible pain of this disease. And in the 1940s they got a chance to pay, when it was found that various forms of the hormone cortisone were very effective in relieving the symptoms of arthritis. (Cortisone is one of the many hormones produced in the outer part, or cortex, of the adrenal gland.) Cortisone had to be extracted from slaughtered animals and the cost was high—as high as fifty dollars for a pill that brought a few hours' relief.

Julian had synthesized a soybean substance that was similar to cortisone but was not quite the same. It differed from cortisone in only one oxygen atom. But that one atom of difference was enough to make Julian's substance, cortexolone, another adrenal cortex secretion, useless as a cortisone substitute. In a brilliant series of experiments, Julian succeeded in putting an oxygen atom in the right place, and the result was synthetic cortisone. The price of the synthetic cortisone was so much less than the natural product, that a pill that had cost as much as fifty dollars now cost only a few cents. Cortisone was found to be effective in the treatment of a variety of functional diseases. Millions of people who had faced a life of pain and suffering because they could not afford medication, which ounce for ounce cost more than gem diamonds, now had relief from pain within financial reach.

But neither Julian's cortisone nor any other medicine could cure the disease of racism afflicting this nation. And once again, his great achievement notwithstanding, he and his family suffered harassment and more humiliation when they attempted to get a little piece of the American dream. Julian bought a home in a suburb of Chicago called Oak Park. Shortly after he moved into the house, someone set it on fire when the Julians were not at home. The fire was discovered by the neighbors, who called the fire department so the damage was not heavy.

A wave of indignation followed the arson attempt. Thousands rallied to the support of the Julians, and editorials in newspapers denounced the bigots who might benefit from Dr. Julian's work but who would deny him his right to live in peace in his own home. Less than a year later, however, a bundle of dynamite was thrown at the Julian home from an automobile. The dynamite exploded at the window of the Julian children's bedroom. Fortunately, most of the energy of the blast was expended away from the house, and the children were shaken up but not injured. Again, there were massive expressions of outrage. But only a few weeks later, Julian was again a victim of racism. He had been invited to be the main speaker at a meeting of scientists at Chicago's Union League Club. But he was informed that the Union League Club did not allow Negroes to take part in any activity there.

Julian continued his work with cortisone and found that the Mexican yam was a better source of cortisone than the soybean. So in 1954 he left Glidden to form his own companies, The Julian Laboratories in Chicago and a branch in Mexico. The initial extractions were carried out at the Mexican plants and the final refining was done in Chicago. In 1961 he sold the enterprise to the pharmaceutical firm of Smith, Kline, and French for $2,338,000 and was retained as president of the new subsidiary.

Julian was now a multimillionaire and widely acclaimed in the chemical industry as a genius in the art of synthesizing organic substances. And, ironically, it had come about largely due to the frightened racism of the academic world in the 1920s. If Julian had been able to proceed unhindered through the usual steps of a scientific academic career, he would have become a professor in a university. He still would have engaged in research (if successful in the scramble for grants) and he would have had a respectable, if less affluent, career.

Julian never lost his love for colleges and universities. He served on the boards of directors of Southern Union, Howard, Fisk, and De Pauw universities. Although there is no doubt that Dr. Julian has "made it," he has not isolated himself from the problems of the millions of black Americans who are still trying to make it. He has supported the NAACP, Dr. Martin Luther King's Southern Christian Leadership Conference, and other organizations, with his counsel and money.

After his cortisone work he was showered with all kinds of honors and recognition—most of which were embarrassing to Julian for they trespassed upon the scientist's need to avoid excessive publicity. Among the accolades were the "Old Gold Goblet Award" from De Pauw University, "Chicagoan of the Year" for 1950, a silver plaque from the National Conference of Christians and Jews, the Merit Award of the Chicago Technical Societies Council, and the American Institute of Chemists' Chemical Pioneer Award. The latter two were from organizations of scientists and were considered by the scientific community to be proper types of awards for a scientist to accept. Some of the others, especially the Chicagoan of the Year, might have been less than comfortable for Julian to accept.

It was on the occasion of the Chicagoan Award that Julian made statements that seemed to sum up the personal tragedy of the black scientist. The press had reported to the general public that Julian was the "discoverer of cortisone." This was certainly not the case, and the newspaper stories were just the sort of thing which can damage a scientist's standing with the academic community. At the Award banquet, Julian did not talk about cortisone, but he made some rather rebutting remarks about what he called "over-exaltation." His remarks included, ". . . I don't know why you honor me such, except that I belong to a race which hangs heavily upon your conscience and you are deifying me before I actually become eligible for the Kingdom of the Gods!"

EPILOGUE

The black scientist has faced formidable obstacles in obtaining the necessary education and then in finding a situation that will enable him to do his work. Once he has established himself, he finds he is not thought of as a scientist but as a "black scientist" and as such is expected to devote much of his time and effort to various social issues, at the expense of his scientific work and privacy. If he does not, he may be accused of being a "Tom" or of shirking a greater responsibility to his race. In this conflict of roles, the scientifically talented black has become what Percy Julian has referred to as the "most poignantly tragic intellectual schizophrenic of the first half of the twentieth century."

The seizures of university buildings and other acts of protest by so-called black militants may be a continued symptom of the intellectual schizophrenia referred to by Julian. The black student feels a responsibility to himself to get an education, but at the same time he feels a responsibility to do something about past and present injustices, about the forces that would keep him confined in the dark "separate but equal" corner of American life, and to the thousands of Americans who are still in that corner.

There are hopeful signs that the "separate but equal" chapter of American history is coming to a close. A generation of young black Americans is enrolled in colleges and universities, and the scientists who will emerge from this generation may not have to suffer the rejections and "intellectual schizophrenia" of the past. They will find their places in the scientific communities of their disciplines and as pure scientists will be no more known to the general public than any other scientists. And this is as it should be. Then, scientists who happen to be black will no longer be so rare that books such as this one will need to be written about them as phenomena. The black scientist, unhampered by pressures from any quarter, will have his "scientific privacy," and he will be free to pursue scientific truth and to add to man's fund of knowledge.

INDEX

INDEX

Aaron E. Klein has taught biology in secondary schools and colleges for over ten years. Born in Atlanta, Georgia, he was educated in public schools in Georgia and Connecticut, the Universities of Pennsylvania and Bridgeport, and Yale and Wesleyan Universities. He participated in the Visiting Scientist Program of the Museum of Art, Science, and Industry in Bridgeport, Connecticut.

He served in the Navy where he edited a newspaper and has since written several science books for young readers. Mr. Klein is a science editor in a large educational publishing house and lives near Boston with his wife and two sons.